Eyes in the Sky

Eyes in the Sky is a work of creative nonfiction. Each of the stories included in this collection is based on actual events. For dramatic and narrative purposes, they may contain some specially created scenes and characters. The names of some individuals have been changed to respect their privacy.

Eyes in the Sky

A Glimpse of the Las Vegas of the Past

As Seen by the Men Who Helped Build It

Karen Leslie

LKC Publications

LKC Publications
2340 Brighton Shore Street
Las Vegas, NV 89128

Copyright © Karen Leslie, 2019

Front cover design: Suzanne Johnson
Cover photo courtesy of UNLV Special Collections
Thanks to Norm Johnson for the use of his image.

ISBN 978-0-9985036-4-6

For the "Mouse Pack,"
Curt, Dan, Gene, Jerry, Kent and Norm.

And for the decades of other unsung heroes
Who worked behind the scenes to transform Las
Vegas into the extraordinary city it is today.

TABLE OF CONTENTS

Prologue

Contents

Prologue

Many stories have been told about Las Vegas: the Bugsy Siegel stories, the Rat Pack stories, the tales of broken knuckles and cement shoes, of showgirls, call girls, and alcohol-induced decadence. But beyond the glitz and glamour of penthouse suites and fancy showrooms, outside smoky casinos where fortunes were won and lost, another Las Vegas operated out of view and undisclosed.

In the pages that follow, six men draw from careers spanning more than half a century to reveal the inner workings of the industry they helped build. They arrived in Las Vegas as ordinary young men, their futures uncertain in an untamed land of dust storms and tumbleweed. But the extraordinary opportunities they encountered as they pursued their dreams rewarded them with rich and unique lives and a special place in the history of one of the most remarkable cities in the world.

By telling their stories with humor and heart, they provide a unique glimpse into the Las Vegas of the past, as seen from their own "eyes in the sky."

Meet Kent Carmichael, Curt Thompson, Norm Johnson, Dan Celeste, Gene Sagas, and Gerald Gillock. Affectionately dubbed "The Mouse Pack," these men saw it all and did it all. Now they're telling it all.

1

For His Next Act

Las Vegas burst on the scene as a Wild West gambling mecca in the '40s and '50s. Mobsters conducted business unencumbered by legal restraints in an untamed environment, transforming Las Vegas from a dusty desert town into the host of a thriving casino industry, swimming in money and surrounded by muscle.

Among the most notorious casino moguls of the time was Benny Binion, owner of Binion's Horseshoe Gambling Hall.

Benny fled to Las Vegas from Texas in 1951 just ahead of the law. He bought the Eldorado Club and the Apache Hotel downtown, combining them into Binion's Horseshoe.

In 1953, the federal government caught up with him. Benny was convicted of tax fraud, and sent to prison.

In late '57, Benny was released from Leavenworth Penitentiary, after serving a three-and-a-half year stretch on a five-year bit. The conviction cost him his gaming license and, days prior to his sentencing, he sold the Horseshoe to old friend Joe W. Brown.

But this was Las Vegas in the glory days of the mob and Benny had friends. A little thing like losing his license couldn't keep a man like him down. There was always a way to work around pesky little problems like Gaming Control.

Shortly after his return to Las Vegas, Benny resumed quietly running the Horseshoe under the title of consultant, with the help of Fremont Hotel owner Ed Levinson, who had purchased the Horseshoe from Brown.

Levinson used the Fremont's licensing to keep the Horseshoe up and running. Handshakes behind closed doors were common and everyone profited in spite of the rules. Although Benny never regained his gaming license, he continued to be the driving force behind the Horseshoe under Levinson's blanket ownership of both casinos.

The transition into the '50s and '60s was a time of adjustment for casinos in downtown Las Vegas as they faced increasing competition from the resorts cropping up out on the Strip. Levinson knew that one of the few ways to lure gamblers away from the Strip "carpet joints" was to provide first-class entertainment in his hotels.

He opened the Carnival Room at the Fremont in 1959 to compete. It was a move that launched the Las Vegas career of a man who would become known worldwide, first as the "The Midnight Idol" and later as "Mr. Entertainment" and "Mr. Las Vegas."

That man was Wayne Newton.

****

Sixteen-Year-Old Wayne

Wayne Newton and his brother Jerry were the first act booked into the newly built Carnival Room lounge. The two kids from Phoenix became a popular draw at the hotel, playing six shows a night, six nights a week, starting at 5 p.m. But the initial booking of the Newtons wasn't without complications.

A few weeks before Wayne's contract was to begin, Fremont entertainment director, Hank Kovell sat across from Levinson and hotel vice-president Eddie Torres in Levinson's office.

Wayne's only sixteen years old," Hank began. "How are we going to square this kid performing in a casino lounge serving alcohol with the Gaming Control Board?"

"We can't," Ed Levinson replied with a frown. "He can't be anywhere near the alcohol or the games."

"Let's get Johnny in here," Torres said. He picked up the phone and summoned Johnny Grandie, hotel facilities director.

"I'll talk to the building department and get the lounge rezoned," Johnny said. "We'll have it annexed as a section of the hotel separate from the bar. As long as the boys stay in their dressing room or on the stage, we should be able to swing it. They can perform at show time and we'll keep them out of the casino between shows."

Levinson gave Johnny a nod. "They're only booked for two weeks. See if you can pull it off."

Johnny secured the required status for the dressing room and stage and Wayne and Jerry began their gig. Six shows a day was a heavy schedule, but much to the delight of casino management, word spread and the Newton brothers began packing the lounge. Their original two-week engagement was extended month after month, ultimately lasting nearly five years.

Although the breaks between shows were short, Wayne had to leave the hotel. The soda fountain at White Cross Drugs across the street served great milkshakes and quickly became his favorite spot while waiting for his next set to begin.

After a full day of executive duties, Torres and Levinson frequently hung out in the Carnival Room. One night a few months into the Newton boys' extended contract, Eddie Torres was heading for the lounge when he saw Wayne heading out the back of the hotel. "How's it going, kid?" Eddie asked. "Everything OK?"

"Well, sir," Wayne answered, "one of the FOH spotlights in the showroom went out at the end of our last show. It left me in the dark. Jerry and I had to do the last number sharing the other spot. Maybe somebody could take a look?"

"Sure thing, kid." Eddie smiled at the polite young man. "You go enjoy your soda. I'll take care of it."

A few minutes later, the phone in the electrical room on the mezzanine level of the hotel rang. The PBX operator was patching Eddie through to the night maintenance man.

That man was a young Kent Carmichael.

****

The Swan Dive

Kent arrived in Las Vegas in the late '50s from California at the tender age of 25 and found work in a growing town that was hungry for skilled labor. He began working for Western Neon Sign Company during the day as a sign hanger. The first sign he installed with Western was the "Welcome to Fabulous Las Vegas" sign, designed by Nevada native Betty Willis in 1959 and sold to Clark County by Western Sign company owner, Ted Rogich, for $4,000. The sign stands to this day as an iconic representation of Las Vegas throughout the world.

Erecting signs in the intense heat of the Las Vegas desert was strenuous work. Even for a young man in great physical shape, it was a grueling occupation that barely paid the bills. In order to better support his wife, daughter, and newborn son, Kent took a night job as an electrician and maintenance man at the Fremont Hotel, adjacent Binion's Horseshoe.

Kent answered the phone, "Carmichael."

"Mr. Carmichael, I have Mr. Torres on the phone for you. Please hold."

"Hi, Kent, It's Eddie. I just saw the Newton kid. He says there's a light out on the stage. Fix it before the next show."

"I'll do it now, Mr. Torres."

"Good." Eddie hung up.

Kent took the stairs from the mezzanine down to the Carnival Room. He wove through the tables and around the bar to the revolving stage, then made his way to the back half of the stage where Wayne and Jerry were set up.

He stopped in front of the electrical panel that worked the stage revolve, the sound, and the lights, all controlled by Wayne while he and Jerry were performing.

Kent turned on the power switch and flipped the eight toggles that controlled the lights assigned to the Newton show. He peeked around the side of the stage to the front of the lounge and looked up. All the lights designated for Wayne and Jerry's show were illuminated, except one. Wayne's center-stage spotlight was out.

"It's probably either the bulb or the fuse," he said to himself.

Kent turned off the lights and headed back upstairs. He made a quick stop to pick up a fuse and a bulb in the electrical room and walked down the hall to the entrance of the "eye in the sky," the labyrinth of catwalks above the casino floor from which surveillance agents watched the action through binoculars and one-way ceiling mirrors in order to catch dishonest employees and players trying to cheat the house. It was a short walk to the attic above the Carnival Room. He proceeded down the narrow catwalk, turning left to take the path toward the area housing the spotlight.

The confined area of the catwalk was dark and narrow, with very little visibility beyond the metal structure immediately beneath his feet. There was no ventilation in the attic and Kent could feel sweat forming on his brow. Midway down, he reached the damaged spotlight and sat down on the catwalk. His feet dangled on either side over the edge, only a few inches from the asbestos ceiling panels of the lounge where the Newton boys performed.

"OK," he mumbled, setting the spare bulb and fuse on his lap, "let's see which it is." He unscrewed the bulb inside the projector fixture and held the fixture in his left hand while he examined the bulb. Even in the dark, he could see the bulb had burnt out. He set the damaged bulb down beside him on the catwalk and was preparing to replace it with the new one when suddenly, a voice from the microphone bellowed through the showroom below, "Ladies and gentlemen," "the Newton Brothers!"

Wayne's voice boomed from the microphone as he hit the stage-revolve button and flipped the eight light toggles on the control board.

Kent felt the surge of 220 volts of electricity from the live projector-fixture wires shoot from his left hand, up his arm, and down through his body. The wires crackled and sparks flew. Kent rocked back, lifting his legs off the metal catwalk in an attempt to insulate himself from the current.

Below, music blasted. Wayne and Jerry sang their opening number as the stage revolved 180 degrees and delivered the duo into the view of the audience.

Above, Kent struggled to stay on the catwalk, but with both feet in the air and live electricity coursing through him, he lost his balance and rolled off the scaffolding.

He was falling. And falling fast.

He hit the asbestos ceiling tiles head first; they broke apart like a Styrofoam piñata.

As his upper body smashed through the ceiling, Kent watched as the floor of the lounge rose up to meet him. He stretched out his arms in a swan dive, snapped his body into a pike position, rolled over onto his back, and flattened out. He could hear screams over the music at the sight of the huge figure falling from out of nowhere as he crashed onto a table.

Kent landed with an enormous thud, flipping the table on its side and sending him to the ground amid a cloud of broken ceiling tiles and asbestos dust. The impact also sent the young couple seated at the table flying backwards.

At the same moment, the stage finished revolving. Wayne and Jerry stood before the crowd with their mouths agape. Alarmed audience members looked on in shock as two cocktail waitresses rushed to the scene and helped the young couple to their feet. They appeared to be dazed, but otherwise unharmed.

Kent, on the other hand, was a sight to behold.

As the dust continued to settle, he rose to his feet. At six feet tall, with his muscular frame covered in white asbestos dust, he looked like a towering albino Paul Bunyan. His work boots, jeans, and short-sleeved shirt were snow white, but his face and forearms, teeming with sweat only moments before, were now completely plastered with white dust.

In his hand, he still held the projector bulb.

Audience members began to laugh hysterically.

"Are you OK?" Wayne said into the microphone.

Kent shook his head, shrugged his shoulders, and threw up his arms, all in embarrassment. The movement filled the air around him in a cloud of white, sparking more laughter from the audience.

Looking on apparently realizing that, other than the ceiling, the mishap had ended with no apparent serious damage, and being the young showman that he was, Wayne seized the moment. Gesturing toward Kent as he leaned into the microphone, he said "Now there, ladies and gentlemen, is a man who knows how to make an entrance."

2

Kent Falls From the Catwalk
To Walk a Tightrope

One of Kent's weekly tasks at the Fremont was to reset the 10 Simplex clocks in the keno station, the room where the keno tickets were written and time-stamped. The room was circular, with individual stations lined up side by side in a circle with the keno-ball machine located in the center. Each station contained a money box into which keno writers deposited money at the end of every shift.

A few days after the Carnival Room swan dive, Kent was resetting the last clock in the row when he noticed the money box at that station had been left unlocked and open. He looked inside the open box. It held a lot of cash.

He looked around. It was Tuesday swing shift and, as was usual on a Tuesday, the room was quiet. He was alone, except for one writer sitting at her station on the other side of the room.

He looked back down at the money, sitting in an open box, waiting to be stolen. Alarm bells went off in his head. He closed the box drawer and walked over to the keno writer. "Please stay here and make sure no one goes near station ten. There's a wiring problem with the clock, and it could be dangerous," he lied through a friendly smile. "I'll be right back."

He left the keno station and called Mike Sarge, the hotel's casino boss.

Kent told Sarge about the open box. "I closed it. I don't want to be accused of stealing any money, but I didn't want to leave it open like that."

"I'll get security on it," Sarge said. "Don't worry. You did the right thing."

The following afternoon, when Kent clocked in for his shift, Mike Sarge was waiting for him. "Ed Levinson wants to see you in his office. There's some kind of problem."

****

The Wire Tap

Ed Levinson did have a problem, a big one. Bad news had come in earlier in the day from the Chicago mob. A paid informant inside the FBI had leaked information about an investigation into skimmed cash at Las Vegas casinos, the Fremont among them.

"How the hell are they getting information?" Eddie Torres asked, pacing in the hallway outside Ed Levinson's office. "Do you think your office is bugged?"

"Well, if it is, we damned well better find out." Levinson grabbed on to Eddie's arm. "Stop pacing. You're making me nervous."

"Yeah, well, I'm nervous, too," Eddie said. "We need to get somebody in there to look around. I know just the guy." He walked back into the office, picked up Levinson's phone, and called Mike Sarge. "When Carmichael comes in to work today, send him to Levinson's office."

Five hours after Eddie's call to Mike Sarge, Kent stood in front of Ed Levinson's desk. Across the room, Eddie Torres stood staring out the office window at the Horseshoe across the street. "You wanted to see me, sir?"

Kent's heart was beating so fast it felt like it might explode. He looked at Levinson, fully expecting to be fired over the keno-station incident the night before.

"Wipe that worried look off your face, kid," Levinson said. "I'm not going to fire you. I know what happened in the keno office."

Levinson noticed a dark bruise on Kent's forehead. "That must've been some fall you had in the Carnival Room a few days ago. I'm glad you weren't hurt too bad. I hear my ceiling didn't fare so well," he added with a chuckle.

Kent's face turned beet red. "The ceiling's been fixed, sir." He rocked back and forth in his work boots with his hands in his pockets. "Is that why I'm here?"

Eddie Torres walked over to the desk and took a seat. "Listen, kid, Ed called you in here because we've got a problem and we need your help." He nodded at Levinson.

"Yes, sir," Kent replied, a wave of relief temporarily passing through him.

"You have a wife and kids, don't you?" Levinson asked, studying the young man fidgeting in front of him.

"I do, sir, a wife, a daughter, and a son," Kent replied.

"Well, how'd you like a nice raise? I need a man I can trust. Can I trust you, kid?"

At the mention of a raise, Kent stopped fidgeting. "You can trust me, sir. Whatever you need."

"Let's take a little walk outside."

Kent followed the two men into the hallway outside Levinson's office. He stood sandwiched between Levinson and Torres, waiting for one of them to speak.

"We think my office may be bugged," Levinson said in a low voice. "If you were going to put a bug in there, where would you put it?"

11

Kent answered without hesitation. "No doubt in the phone."

"Uh-huh," Eddie Torres said. "If you opened the phone, would you know what to look for?"

"Sure," Kent replied. "I'm very familiar with the phone system."

"OK," Levinson said. "Let's go back inside. I want you to take my phone apart. If you see something, don't say a word. Just put the phone back together. Then we'll come back out here and talk."

The men returned to the office.

Kent lifted the phone base, pulled a screwdriver from his tool belt, and opened the bottom of the base.

He saw it immediately. A tiny microphone was lodged inside and he pointed to it. Levinson and Torres, hovering nearby, leaned in to take a look. With a swirl of his finger, Levinson gestured for Kent to close up the phone base, then pointed to the door.

Once outside, Torres exploded. "Goddamn it. I knew it!" He looked at Kent. "Is that damned thing working all the time?"

Kent's shoulders lifted in a shrug. "I'd need to check the wiring to answer that question, sir. The wires lead to the F assembly room."

Torres raised an eyebrow. "What's that?"

"It's the room that contains all the equipment servicing the entire property's phone system. It's all supplied by the phone company."

Levinson looked at Torres. "We've got to go somewhere else to talk, somewhere outside the hotel. Come on, kid." He nodded at Kent. "We're going to the garage."

A few minutes later, the three men stood in front of Eddie Torres' 1953 Cadillac. It was parked in a dark corner

12

of the Fremont Hotel garage. Torres leaned his six-three frame against the hood of his Cadillac while Levinson interrogated Kent.

"The phone company does all the work in there, right?"

"Yes, sir."

"Isn't that phone room locked up all the time?"

"Yes, sir."

"In case of a fire, who on property has a key?"

"That would be Mr. Grandie."

"OK, kid. Here's what we want you to do." He looked over at Torres, whose arms were crossed in front of his body. The irritation that showed on his face traveled all the way down his huge frame to his right foot, which was tapping rapidly on the garage floor. It was an intimidating sight. Torres looked every bit the gangster he was.

Levinson gave Kent a look that made his blood run cold. "Listen. You're going to do what I tell you and you're going keep your mouth shut. Understand?"

"Yes, sir. Absolutely, sir."

"Check that wiring. It has to lead somewhere. If there's a recording device, find it. And go see the casino manager and get our flash camera. Photograph everything in that room. The whole damned place. If you see anything that doesn't belong there, I want it photographed." He flicked his hand in the direction of the casino like he was shooing away a fly. "Get going."

"Yes, sir."

Levinson and Torres watched as Kent rushed off.

"This is a mess, Ed," Torres said, slamming his fist on the hood of his car. "A goddamned mess."

****

Kent entered the F assembly room. On racks attached to the walls, aisles of wiring assemblies filled the room. Each assembly serviced a different area of the hotel and casino.

He turned the latch that opened one of the panel doors, exposing hundreds of color-coded wires. Looms of thirty-plus wires were grouped together in clumps throughout the panel.

He rummaged through the panel until he located the looms of wires marked "Executive Office." His fingers maneuvered through the maze of wiring, carefully separating the looms to isolate the wiring loom coming in from Levinson's office. He followed the loom out.

Twelve inches along the way, he discovered eight wires veering off to a higher location in the panel box. The remaining wires continued on to the circuit board.

Kent's eyes followed the path of the eight wires. When he discovered their final destination, his eyes got big. He saw that cleverly nestled behind a cluster of wires and hidden from view were two tape recorders.

He reached for the casino flash camera and began taking pictures. As he photographed the recorders and the eight renegade wires, satisfaction over his discovery mingled with fear. A shiver went up his spine as he remembered a scene from an old Cagney mob movie. Some poor schmuck had delivered bad news to Cagney. Angered by what he heard, Cagney shot the guy dead.

Kent gulped. He hoped with every beat of his pounding heart that Levinson and Torres weren't going to shoot the messenger.

"I'll be a son of a bitch," Torres said to Levinson, as they fingered the photos spread out on the desk in front of them.

"Take it easy, Eddie." Levinson placed his index finger over his lips. He looked across the desk at Kent. "Good work, kid. You're done here. You'll get that raise I promised. But remember what I said." His voice lowered to a whisper. "We expect your loyalty. And your silence. You know nothing."

****

Mobsters Have Rights Too

There was, in fact, a lot Kent didn't know, starting with Levinson's past.

Ed Levinson was one of the investors who opened the Sands Hotel way out on the incipient Strip in December 1952. He was on the California Crime Commission's list of individuals, including the likes of well-known gangster Meyer Lansky, trying to become established in legal gambling. Nevada had a unique way of determining eligibility that differed from California law, which strictly prohibited gambling. The Nevada Gaming Commission distinguished between legal licensed gamblers and unlicensed racketeers. Although Levinson was identified as a bookmaker, he was, according to the Gaming Commission, "thoroughly scrutinized" prior to being granted his casino permit.

Levinson had managed Meyer Lansky's Havana Riviera nightclub in Cuba during the late '50s until Castro came into power and closed the casino in 1959. He then returned to Las Vegas to run the Fremont, with Eddie Torres as vice-president. Under Levinson's licensing, the mob continued to run the casino.

It was discovered that the recorders Kent found in the F assembly room led to a special telephone line leased to the Henderson Novelty Company, a front constructed by the FBI to conduct electronic surveillance.

Levinson sued the FBI agents for $2 million, naming the Central Telephone Company as another defendant, because its employees cooperated with the feds in installing the microphones. Levinson won both cases.

****

Kent, Jack, and Benny

A few months after the phone-tap episode, Kent got another call to report to Levinson's office.

"Something's come up. Benny Binion's short on maintenance workers over at the Horseshoe, so I'm going to need you to work between both hotels. You'll still be on the Fremont payroll, but you'll also be working with Benny's people."

Kent took a deep breath. He felt a lump forming in his throat as his heart started beating rapidly. Stories about Benny's days in Texas were common among the employees of both the Fremont and Horseshoe. Every time Benny was spotted in the Fremont visiting Levinson, the casino filled with whispered stories about his past.

Kent had heard a few. Benny killed a guy in Texas, then shot himself to claim self-defense. He ran illegal moonshine and numbers rackets in Dallas and gunned down the competition. The man had done time at Leavenworth. Benny was a gangster, plain and simple, a fact that put the fear of God into Horseshoe employees and made Fremont employees grateful they weren't working across the street.

"Will I be working directly with Mr. Binion?" Kent's voice cracked on the word "directly."

"Relax, kid. You'll be answering to me." Levinson tapped on his desk. "Pull up a chair. Here's what we're going to do."

Levinson explained that a facility was to be constructed in the garage of the Fremont Hotel to house an IBM computer system. The state-of-the-art contraption would monitor slot machine activity in the entire casino.

"We're going to dig a tunnel beneath Third Street, connecting the Fremont to the basement of the Horseshoe," Levinson said. "Once that's completed, you'll have some wiring to do. I'll tell you more once the tunnel's completed."

Kent remained silent. He couldn't stop thinking about all the stories he'd heard about Benny.

The project began and Kent's work load was divided between the two hotels. Backhoes dug the hole and cables were run through the tunnel between the Fremont and the Horseshoe. Binion's slot activity was hooked up to the machine to monitor wins and losses, in addition to those at the Fremont. Within a few months, profits and losses from both casinos were being monitored in tandem.

Kent not only worked on building the original Fremont-garage facility, he also pitched in on the tunnel and the subsequent link-up of the two casinos. He reported back to Levinson on a regular basis and had limited exposure to Benny.

During this time, he developed a close personal friendship with Benny's son, Jack Binion. Jack was the polar opposite of his dad. He had a light-hearted personality and a genuine zest for life. Jack later became owner of the Horseshoe, along with his sister Becky.

As Kent's friendship with Jack grew, he continued to steer clear of Benny.

One day in 1963, out of the blue, things changed.

3

The Deacon's Bench

"Hey, Carmichael, get over here," Ed Daniels, head engineer at the Horseshoe, hollered over the rows of clanging slot machines lining the main casino floor. "The boss wants to see you."

Kent felt a sudden chill run up his spine. He crossed the casino floor and stopped in front of Daniels. "Benny? Why?"

"Beats me. He just told me to find you and get you over to his booth in the coffee shop, pronto," Ed replied, shaking his head. "You know Benny. He doesn't like to wait."

"He wants to see me now?" Kent could feel his palms getting sweaty.

"No, he wants to see you five minutes ago. I'd get over there quick if I were you."

Kent made a beeline to the coffee shop. He spotted Benny sitting in his corner booth, smoking a cigar and talking to one of the pit bosses. As he approached the table, he noticed the handle of a shotgun peeking out from the back cushion and resting beside Benny. "You wanted to see me, Mr. Binion?" Kent asked.

Benny took a puff from his cigar and motioned to an empty spot in the booth. "Sit down, kid." Kent took a seat and waited for Benny to finish his business. Once the pit boss left the table, Benny turned to face Kent. "I understand Jack had you over to do work on the house a couple of days ago. He told me you two are friends and that you've got a little sign maintenance company. Makes you a little extra money, I imagine." He paused to take another puff on his cigar. His eyes were glued on Kent.

Kent felt the hairs on the back of his neck stand erect. He'd just finished repairs on the air-conditioning unit at the Binion home on Bonanza and Tonopah. He'd returned the house key to Arlene, the housekeeper, and left the property, job done. He took a deep breath. "I got your air working a few days ago and yes, I do have a small sign maintenance company. But I only work at night, after my shift here at the hotel's over. It doesn't interfere with—"

Benny cut him off. "Relax, kid. You aren't in any trouble. I just have some questions." He smiled through the cigar smoke engulfing the table.

Kent felt the knot in his stomach relax at the sight of Benny's poker face softening into a smile.

"Building those signs, do you work with steel? I mean, can you weld?" Benny waved the hand holding his cigar in the air, motioning a waitress over to the booth. "You want a bowl of chili?"

"I'm fine, thank you, Mr. Binion."

"Call me Benny."

"Yes, sir, Benny, and no, sir, I'm good." He glanced over at the shotgun. The knot in his stomach was back.

The waitress arrived at the booth. "What can I get you, Mr. Binion?" she asked.

Benny winked at the waitress. He'd given her the nickname Little Red, due to her short stature and flaming red hair. He patted his stomach. "Carmichael here'll have a bowl of our famous chili."

"Yes, Mr. Binion." Little Red returned the wink and hurried off to fetch the chili. It was common knowledge that Benny loved the stuff. He ordered it for everyone who sat with him at his booth, like it or not.

"So, do you? Weld?" Benny repeated.

"Yes, sir, we work with all kinds of steel in the sign business. I'm an experienced welder."

"Good. I want you to build me a four-sided, solid-steel, deacon's bench and I want it welded together. You got a tape measure on you?"

Kent pulled his tape measure off his tool belt and handed it to Benny.

Benny stretched the tape out. "I want it twenty-nine inches tall and thirty-three inches deep." He set the tape measure back on the table. "And I want it six feet long."

"A steel bench that large will be heavy. Do you mean sheet metal?" Kent asked.

"Hell, no!" Benny boomed. "I want it out of *steel*. I don't give a damn how heavy it is."

The knot in Kent's stomach tightened. "I'm sorry. I understand. Steel, of course."

"And one more thing," Benny added. "I want a steel bottom and a top seat that hinges up so I can put things inside the bench."

"Yes, sir," Kent replied, his heart racing. Benny's face was red. He was a powder keg just waiting to explode.

At the sight of Little Red approaching, Benny calmed down.

She set the chili in front of Kent and smiled at Benny. "Anything else, Mr. Binion?"

"No, doll." His eyes followed Little Red until she was out of sight, then he turned his attention back to Kent. "Eat your chili and meet me in front of the accounting room upstairs in fifteen minutes. I'll show you where I want it." He rose from the booth and left the coffee shop.

Kent looked past his bowl of chili across the table. The handle of the shotgun was still visible, sticking out from the back of the booth. He picked up his spoon and started eating.

Fifteen minutes later, the elevator opened on the second floor. Kent walked out into the narrow hallway and down to the door of the accounting room. He bent down to tap on the brittle floor. The Horseshoe casino was located on the first floor of the Apache Hotel and the entire building was old. Originally built in 1911, the floor was made of plywood and the outer walls were built with adobe blocks. There was no way the second floor of the building would support a heavy steel bench. Kent shuddered at the thought of having to tell Benny that his bench would most certainly fall through the floor into the casino below.

The elevator door opened again and Benny exited into the hallway. "OK, Carmichael, let me show you where I want my bench." He hit the security buzzer for access to the accounting room. He looked up at the security camera installed above the door.

The door unlocked with the sound of another buzz. A security guard opened the door and the two men entered.

Benny walked over to a wall to the left of the door and pointed. "Here. I want it right here."

Kent took a deep breath. "Mr. Binion, I'm afraid we have a problem."

"What is it, Carmichael?" Benny remained uncharacteristically calm.

Kent breathed a sigh of relief. "It's about how heavy the bench will be. These old floors won't be able to handle the weight. We're talking close to four hundred pounds." Kent waited for Benny's response.

Benny turned to the security guard. "What's below us?"

The guard shook his head. "I'm not sure, boss. The cage, I think."

"Carmichael, you figure out what's beneath this spot and report back to me. I expect to hear from you within the hour. I'll be in the coffee shop." Benny left the accounting room.

Kent pulled out his tape measure and blocked out the location of the proposed bench in relation to the elevator. He rode the elevator back to the first floor, pulled out his measurements, and retraced his blocking. The bench would be located directly overhead from a spot 10 feet directly in front of the cage window. The news was good. He headed for the coffee shop to tell Benny.

"If we place two six-inch-square steel support tubes floor to ceiling in the casino, six feet apart and ten feet in front of the cage, the bench will be safe." Knowing of Benny's love of beveled mirrors, he added, "And it'll be easy enough to cover the sides of the tubes with six-inch mirrors, creating square mirrored columns."

"Mirrors," Benny said. "I love it. Get the maintenance crew on it right away."

The mirrored columns were up in less than a week. But now it was time for Kent to address the problems with how the bench would be built. "We'll have to bring the steel plates up one at a time in the elevator and assemble it in the accounting room."

"We?"

"Yes, sir. It'll take three or four men to lift them. Once they're up there, I can start welding them together."

Benny stood admiring the mirrored columns, cigar stub clenched between his teeth. He didn't bat an eyelash before he said, "Whatever you need. Just get it done."

Accounting was open 24/7, with day and swing shifts buzzing with activity. In order to minimize the issue of limited space in the room, graveyard-shift employees were the lucky ones chosen to suffer the sounds and smells of the bench being welded together just a few feet away. Once Kent had placed an asbestos sheet on the carpet where the bench would rest, he joined Ed Daniels and two other members of the maintenance crew in the Horseshoe basement, where the steel plates were placed when they arrived from the fabricator. The four men carried the first plate into the elevator and up to the hallway leading to the accounting room. Once inside the room, they maneuvered the plate into position.

"This sucker's heavy," a crew member said, straining his back as he held his corner of the plate over the asbestos sheeting.

"Be careful setting it in place," Kent advised the crew. "Mr. Binion was clear about getting it flush up against the wall."

Kent held one corner of the plate and directed the men as they squatted down to set it over the asbestos sheeting.

"You'd better be careful not to burn Benny's wall," Ed cautioned, looking over at the pile of welding tools resting a few feet from the plate. "I don't envy you this job."

Kent wiped the sweat from his brow with the sleeve of his shirt. "I feel sorry for the employees working this shift," he said, gesturing to the count-room employees sitting less than three yards away from the wall where the maintenance crew had delivered the first plate. Sparks were going to fly. "It's nearly one a.m. Let's go down and get the back plate. Once it's in place, I can start welding."

Kent put on his mask and gloves and turned on the welder. Sparks sprayed in an arc of light into the air. He looked through his mask at the nervous faces staring across the short distance to the counting tables. The vibration from the welder shook the old flooring, raising the eyebrows of employees as coins rattled and stacks of money shook on the tables in front of them.

Over the years, Kent had grown accustomed to the high-pitched whirring of the welder. But in this constricted space, the shrill sound bounced off the walls, screeching like fingernails on a chalkboard. The employees worked on in resigned, miserable silence.

Benny visited every night during the welding process, arriving unannounced in the wee hours and putting the fear of God into everyone working in the accounting room. He paced in the small area between the accounting tables and the developing bench, smoking his cigar a little too close to the sparks flying from the welder.

"Don't let me bother you, Carmichael," he said, leaning in to get a closer look.

Kent continued working and pretended Benny's hovering wasn't a distraction. He focused on the hinge on the back plate. Benny had insisted on a heavy-duty hinge for the lid and two heavy railroad hasps to lock it down. Kent had welded the hinge to the back plate prior to hauling it up to be welded to the bottom plate.

Benny supplied the railroad hasps himself, explaining their origin as he handed them to Kent. "I got these from Doby Doc. They came right off a car from the Eureka-Nevada Railway."

Everybody who'd lived in Las Vegas for any period of time knew all about Doby Doc. He was not only a close friend of Benny's, but also notorious in his own right for any number of shady dealings, major theft among them. He had, in his words, "taken possession" of an engine and other rolling stock and created his own train in Elko. The hasps came off one of the cars.

Kent set the hasps aside. They'd be welded on last, after the bench was complete and met with Benny's approval.

Welding lasted three nights. Once the lid was positioned on the top of the bench, Kent welded it to the hinge. Finally, the bench sat ready for Benny to decide where he wanted the railroad hasps to go.

Kent was packing up his tools when Benny returned. Benny paced in front of the bench, chomping on his cigar. An inch-long ash rested at the end of the butt. "I've changed my mind," he said.

Kent's jaw dropped. He looked at the man in disbelief.

"Forget the locks. Once I get it filled, I want the whole thing welded shut." Benny flicked his ash onto the accounting-room floor.

"But Mr. Binion," Kent said, "that could be a real problem."

Benny looked surprised. "Why?" he asked.

"Well, welding the lid on is going to create sparks. Whatever's inside, if it's flammable, it'll burn. If I may ask, what's going inside?"

Benny stopped pacing. He pulled Kent out of earshot of the employees working in the room. "Canvas bags, that's all. Is it a problem?"

Kent paused before answering. He'd heard rumors about money going into the bench. "Well, canvas burns, Mr. Binion. So does money."

Benny's eyebrows lifted. "What if it's just coins inside the bags?" His voice lowered. "Silver dollars—but you didn't hear that and you'll never repeat it. Not ever. Not to anyone." Benny's poker face was back.

Kent thought about Benny's sawed-off shotgun and all the stories he'd heard about what happened when Benny got mad. He thought about his wife and small children. He turned to Benny. "I can place sheets of asbestos over the bags. It'll keep the sparks from igniting them." Kent saw Benny's jaw muscles tighten as he chomped down on his cigar.

"Fine. You come back tomorrow night. The bench will be loaded by the time you get here." Benny gave Kent a hearty pat on the back. "Good job, Carmichael." Benny left the accounting room, still clenching the cigar between his teeth.

When Kent arrived on the last night of the bench project, Benny was waiting. The bench was filled to the top with rows of canvas bags. Kent placed the sheets of asbestos on top of the pile. He looked over at Benny, who nodded a go-ahead.

"OK, guys." Kent gestured to the two security guards who had been watching over the bench's cargo. "Help me drop this lid. It's heavy."

Benny watched as the three men positioned themselves in front of the bench and strained to drop over eighty pounds of heavy steel into place.

Kent worked for five hours, welding the bench lid closed. Sparks flew in cascades of light, just as they had during the entire welding process. Once he was finished, he gathered up his tools and went home. It was four o'clock in the morning.

He never entered the accounting room after that day and never saw the bench again.

****

Hi-Ho Silver
Stories abound about the Binion silver dollars. The death of Benny's younger son Ted was linked to reports of millions in silver buried in the desert and dug up in

Pahrump, a small town 60 miles west of Las Vegas, years after Benny died. Could they have been the same silver dollars Benny had so carefully protected in his deacon's bench decades before?

Back in the early years of Las Vegas gaming, money disappeared in a variety of ways. Sometimes it left Las Vegas in a briefcase, handcuffed to the wrist of a visiting Chicago mobster or bag lady. Sometimes it landed in a safety deposit box at a local bank or a vault in the home of a casino boss living behind steel doors at the Las Vegas Country Club.

Some of the tall tales told about the Binion family are true. Some are not. But one fact remains: A deacon's bench filled with silver dollars sat for a time in the accounting room on the second floor of the Apache Hotel, directly above the Horseshoe Casino. And Kent Carmichael is one of the few people living who knows it ever existed, much less what it contained.

****

Opportunity Knocks

In the two years that followed, Kent continued to split time between his sign maintenance company and his job at the two hotels. The city was growing and the dusty gambling town transforming into a municipality, with schools, suburbs, banks and retail stores being built to accommodate a growing population. Small businesses were not only sprouting everywhere, but beginning to thrive.

One evening while Kent was servicing a new Texaco sign on the Strip, a man approached him. He tapped on the side of Kent's ladder and identified himself. "My name's John Papais. I'm a sign man. Can I talk to you for a minute?"

Kent stepped down from the ladder. He extended his hand. "My name's Kent. What can I do for you?"

John Papais stood at six-two. He was slender with strong Italian features. His handshake was warm and confident.

"I've got a sign company in Stockton, California," he began. "We just built a new pylon sign in California for the Sans Souci Hotel in Las Vegas, but now that it's here, the building department won't issue us a permit to hang the damned thing." He offered a mildly apologetic smile over his use of profanity. "If I don't find someone who holds a QE license in the state of Nevada, my sign won't go up." He paused. "Do you happen to have one?"

"Actually, I do," Kent replied. He'd earned his license as a "qualified employee" shortly after his arrival in Las Vegas by passing difficult tests, thus enabling him to open his sign business. "What do you have in mind?"

Papais placed his hands squarely on his hips and looked directly into Kent's eyes. "I'd like to offer you a job. I need a QE to help me set up a new branch here in Vegas. I'll make you manager and pay you more than you're making now, whatever it is. Are you interested?"

The memory of the day he hung the "Welcome to Fabulous Las Vegas" sign flashed in Kent's mind. So much growth had occurred since then. The inevitable was happening. A new sign business was opening its doors in Las Vegas and with it, an opportunity to advance his career in the business he loved.

In late 1965 with Ed Levinson's blessing, Kent quit his hotel job to become manager and QE of Ad-Art, owned by John and Lou Papais, which was about to become one of the largest sign companies in Las Vegas.

Less than a year after opening its doors, thanks to Ed Levinson and Eddie Torres, Ad-Art landed sign contracts at the expanding Riviera Hotel-Casino. The following year, Curt Thompson and Dan Celeste arrived in Las Vegas.

4

Curt Gets a Ride from a Superstar

As the world of Las Vegas gaming continued to expand in the '50s and '60s, the city exploded with the construction of new hotels lining the Strip. With it came a new set of problems for the growing metropolis.

Already lining the Strip, from south to north, were the Hacienda, Tropicana, Flamingo, Frontier, Sands, Stardust, Riviera, Thunderbird, and Sahara. More huge projects, including Caesars Palace, were either in the planning stages or under way, and qualified hospitality-industry professionals were a scarcity. East Coast hotel-management graduates could barely accommodate the growing need.

The key to solving the problem lay in education.

In 1967, Dan Celeste and Curt Thompson were accepted into Paul Smith's College, a hotel-management school in the Adirondack Mountains in upstate New York, a half-hour from Lake Placid. The school was located at the foot of Easy Street Hill, the irony of which was not lost on the students, as brutal winter temperatures that year reached fifty below zero without a wind-chill factor and much of the state was pummeled with severe ice storms.

One winter day while Dan and Curt were in class, their professor, Harry Purchase, announced that Jerry Vallen, his former classmate at Cornell, was opening a hotel-management school in Las Vegas, Nevada. As dean of the new school, Vallen was looking for transfers.

That day the weather was so cold, the thought of moving from a frigid snow-covered forest to a warm desert climate was too much for Curt to resist. He raised his hand like a lightning bolt, followed immediately by the hand of his roommate Dan.

"I'll go," Curt said.

"Me, too. I'll go." Dan echoed.

So the two young men made the trek to Las Vegas to continue their hotel-management education at Nevada Southern University (now UNLV). It was the first hotel-management course to be offered at the university, established specifically to satisfy the city's growing needs. Dan and Curt were two of 15 members in that first class. There are presently more than 15,000 graduates.

Newly relocated and sharing an apartment on Lulu Street near the campus, the boys were still starving students, but at least they weren't freezing their young asses off. They squeaked by, taking advantage of $1.99 casino buffets, where they could afford to eat one meal a day. Neither complained, because the food was good and the price was right.

On Thanksgiving afternoon, Curt and Dan sat surrounded by textbooks at the breakfast table of their tiny apartment.

Dan looked out the kitchen window at the oleander bushes blooming outside. "Thanksgiving and no snow. It must be eighty degrees out there."

"Yeah," Curt said, "and to top it off, we're going to get a home-cooked meal." A fellow student's parents had invited them over for turkey dinner. He closed his textbook. "I'm off. I'll pick up a hostess gift and meet you at the

Taglianetti's house at five." He rose from the table and headed for the door.

At a little after 4 p.m., Curt drove the beat-up Chevy he and Dan shared to the Strip shopping center across the street from the Sahara Hotel. He parked the car in the parking lot between Honest John's Casino and the center's drug store, and crossed his fingers. The Chevy was notorious for overheating and stalling out. When it did, he or Dan would have to wait for it to cool down, sometimes for 30 minutes or longer, before the vehicle would restart.

Curt popped into the drug store, bought a box of candy with what little cash he had in his wallet, and headed back to the Chevy. He got in the car and turned the key.

Nothing.

His heart sank.

"Please start, baby," he pleaded as he turned the key a second time.

Nothing.

After several unsuccessful attempts to start the vehicle, Curt dropped his head onto the steering wheel. "Just my luck," he muttered to himself. The thought of missing out on a home-cooked meal was almost as depressing as the knowledge that the Chevy was undoubtedly on its last legs.

As he sat bemoaning his bad luck and waiting for the car to cool down, he noticed a bright orange Corvette parked next to him in the parking lot. Curt looked over at the stranger in the driver's seat.

The man sitting inside wore a Nehru jacket with strings of beads hanging from the shoulders of the fabric. He was smiling at Curt.

Curt stared at the man, barely believing his eyes. He was just a starving student in a city of stars and now one of the biggest and brightest was sitting only a few feet away from him. "My gosh," he whispered to himself. "That's Sammy Davis Jr."

Sammy's left hand rested on the steering wheel. His fingers were covered in sparkling diamond rings. A flashy diamond-encrusted watch wrapped around his wrist.

Curt had seen many photos of Sammy in magazines and newspapers. He'd also seen him on television, always decked out in diamonds. The man was nearly as famous for his love of jewelry as he was for his talent. There was no mistaking him.

"What's up, man?"

"Well, I'm supposed to be someplace for Thanksgiving dinner and my car's overheated. I'm going to be late, if I make it at all."

"Let me give you a ride," Sammy said.

"Oh, no," Curt replied. "You're Sammy Davis Jr."

Sammy laughed. "Yeah, man. I know. Hop in anyway. Let me give you a lift. It's Thanksgiving."

"Really?" Curt's eyes opened wide behind his glasses. "OK, thanks."

"No problem. Jump in."

Curt left his beat-up Chevy behind and as soon as he'd settled into the plush leather passenger seat of the Corvette, Sammy peeled rubber out of the parking lot. Curt was delighted; the car wasn't only beautiful, it was fast. As the Corvette sped down the Strip, the two men engaged in small talk about Curt's studies at the university and Sammy's love of Vegas.

When they reached the Taglianetti's home, Curt leaned across the car to shake Sammy's hand. "I can't thank you enough, Mr. Davis."

"My pleasure, man. And Curt, it's Sammy. Happy Thanksgiving."

Approaching the front door of the house, Curt saw Dan standing with a group of people staring out the bay window and watching as the Corvette pulled out of the driveway and disappeared down the street.

"Was that who I think it was?" Dan asked as Curt entered the home.

"Yep," Curt replied, snickering at the flabbergasted look on his friend's face. "I just got a ride from a superstar. Sammy Davis Jr. himself."

****

Paying It Forward

Twenty years later, Curt Thompson was the executive vice-president of the Frontier, highly successful in hotel administration. One of his many duties as VP was to book the entertainment for the main showroom when its headliners, Siegfried and Roy, were on vacation.

Booking an act that would come close to equaling the draw of Siegfried and Roy was no simple feat. At the conclusion of every performance featuring the famous duo and their stage full of tigers, customers flooded into the casino to gamble. The Frontier's gaming revenue depended heavily on the power of its entertainers to attract a crowd.

Curt called a booking agency in L.A. and asked for a list of available entertainers. When the list arrived, he scanned the names and stopped short when he saw one of them. There was no need to look further for an act.

The name was Sammy Davis Jr.

Curt picked up his phone and dialed the agency, a broad smile on his face. Booking the star would give him a chance to pay back an act of kindness shown him years before, when he was a struggling student, far from family on Thanksgiving Day. "This is Curt Thompson, VP at the

Frontier Hotel in Las Vegas. Connect me with a booking agent, please."

A few months later, the Frontier marquee sparkled with the name of the legendary singer, dancer, musician, actor, and comedian, noted for his dead-on impressions of celebrities, whose career in show business started at the age of three in vaudeville with his father, Sammy Davis Sr.. It was opening night of his engagement at the Frontier.

The crowd was filing into the showroom as Curt headed backstage to the green room to welcome the entertainer. Sammy was at the peak of his stardom and his entire engagement had sold out almost immediately after the dates were announced. But foremost on Curt's mind at that moment was something entirely different. "I wonder if he'll remember me?" he asked himself.

He entered the green room. It was packed with Sammy's entourage, invited guests, and select members of the press. Curt approached Sammy, who was standing behind the bar. He extended his hand, carefully avoiding Sammy's lit Camel cigarette resting in a Waterford crystal ashtray on the bar.

Curt introduced himself as the Frontier executive VP. "Mr. Davis, I know you aren't going to remember, but twenty years ago you helped out a young man in a broken-down car on Thanksgiving Day. That young man was me."

Curt felt the handshake grow stronger and warmer. And Sammy's eyes sparkled as brightly as the strand of Cartier diamonds resting on his neck. "Of course I remember you. It was a Chevy, wasn't it? And a pretty beat-up one, if I remember correctly. How was that dinner?"

"The best Thanksgiving dinner I ever had, thanks to you," Curt replied. "I've never forgotten it."

"It was just a chance to pay it forward, man," Sammy replied. "Karma's gonna get us all, one way or the

35

other. Cats like me just do what we can to swing things in the right direction and hope for the best."

The stage manager knocked on the open door to announce 10-minute call.

"Have a great show, Mr. Davis," Curt said, as he and Sammy's entourage left the room.

As the house lights dimmed, Curt joined the other Hughes corporate executives in one of the showroom's King's Row booths. Strains of music filled the air as the curtain opened to reveal a huge orchestra stretched across the stage.

"Ladies and gentlemen, Sammy Davis Jr.," the announcement bellowed from the speakers.

The room filled with applause when Sammy appeared from the wings. He walked to a microphone center stage in front of the orchestra.

The show began and Curt sat amid a captivated audience, mesmerized by the phenomenal talent and charisma emanating from the stage. Memories of his days as a college student, of that overheated Chevy and a stranger's kindness on Thanksgiving, flooded back.

By choosing Sammy's name from the list, their chance encounter so many years before had come full circle. Sammy was right: Pay it forward and leave the rest to karma.

Curt Thompson, VP of the Frontier Hotel in the Entertainment Capital of the World, settled back in the booth. He was surrounded by his peers, all of them successful and powerful men. He took a sip of champagne and smiled.

Karma indeed.

5

Someday Country Music Will Catch On

Curt's career blossomed after graduation from UNLV. Several years prior to becoming VP at the Frontier, Curt began a gradual climb up the corporate ladder, working in hotel management within the Del Webb properties. First, he held a position as night manager at the Sahara.

After a short time paying his dues working late hours on swing shift, he was promoted to the position of hotel manager at the Mint on Fremont Street in downtown Las Vegas, also a Del Webb property.

It was at the Mint where Curt first met Norm Johnson, the hotel's director of publicity, and a lifelong friendship began.

Norm was born in Burbank, California, and grew up in Hollywood. Upon his release from military service in the U. S. Air Force, he began working in public relations in southern California, eventually becoming a reporter and sports writer for Copley News Service. He was nominated for a Pulitzer Prize in 1965 for his coverage of the riots in the Watts neighborhood of Los Angeles, an honor that enabled his move to Las Vegas when he was hired by Hank Greenspun to work at the *Las Vegas Sun* as assistant sports editor and featured columnist.

Two years later, in 1967, he was hired by the Mint to take charge of the publicity department.

Eyes in the Sky

During the early days of Las Vegas, the hotels realized there was a need for a way to officially send photos and special events news out to the world. In 1947, hotel executives and publicists got together and created the Las Vegas News Bureau. It was staffed by a couple of former reporters and a few photographers and financed through a fund to which all of the Las Vegas hotels and casinos contributed. The creation of the Bureau enabled casinos to advertise their amenities and special events in sometimes unusual ways, via photographs. Such was the case for Norm one night in 1968 at the Top of the Mint.

As a Mint executive, Norm often met with a number of other executives in the early evening at the bar and restaurant on the 24th floor of the Mint tower, where a live band and a singer were always part of the ambience. It was Happy Hour in its finest form, Las Vegas style. The Top of the Mint featured a gourmet restaurant, manned by Sean Grady, one of the top maître d's in Las Vegas during the 1960s-'70s.

Shortly after 7 p.m., Norm sat beside Bill Bennett, general manager of the Mint, enjoying the music. As the two listened to a beautiful young singer by the name of Lorraine Perry, Norm happened to look out at the view of the Strip from where he was sitting—and was startled by what he saw. Via a unique combination of lighting and the angle he was looking from, a vision of Ms. Perry appeared, hanging out over the Strip.

"Holy shit," Norm exclaimed. "Bill, you have to see what I'm seeing." Norm stood and offered his chair to Bennett. "Sit down here and take a look."

"Must be something pretty damned special to get you out of your chair," Bennett said, his tone playful. "This better be worth it to get me out of mine." Bennett rose from the table and took Norm's seat.

"There. Look there."

"Oh my God," Bennett said, his eyes opening wide." That's the craziest thing I've ever seen. Any way we can capture that?"

Norm's eyes lit up. "So, you can see it?" he asked.

"Damned right." Bennett leaned to he left and right. His eyes were glued to Ms. Perry. "Norm, get that shot. Call the News Bureau. Do whatever you have to do. Just get it."

The following morning, Norm made the call. He asked to speak with Don Payne, manager of the News Bureau. "Don, Norm here. I've got an idea for a great publicity shot up in the Top of the Mint. Could you please send me your best photographer? He'll have to be here at seven p.m. tonight so he can see for himself what I have in mind."

"You got it, buddy."

That night, Jerry Abbott, the Bureau's news-beat photographer, found Norm at the bar looking out the windows toward the Strip as Lorraine sang.

There was the vision.

Jerry saw it clearly. "She looks like she's floating over the Strip," he said, holding his hands in front of him, palms up, thumbs together, framing the shot. "That's some illusion. We've gotta capture that."

They agreed that he'd try to shoot it the following evening. They asked Lorraine to wear a white gown.

Arriving at 6 p.m., Jerry Abbott and the Mint engineer, Fred Sikorsky, worked on setting up the lighting. Then Jerry positioned his three cameras. Lorraine arrived early, looking radiant in a white-chiffon gown.

Lorraine took her position in front of the window. "Let's take a few test shots," Jerry said, loading up his Polaroid Instamatic.

Lorraine, ever the consummate professional, changed position as Jerry directed, in order to place her in perfect lighting for the shot and, at about 7:15 p.m., the cameras were clicking.

Lorraine moved gracefully, spreading her arms to create the illusion of floating, while Jerry moved from camera to camera, snapping away. Eventually, he felt he had captured the shot.

"Great job, everyone," Jerry said, as he packed up his cameras.

Norm gave Lorraine, who was standing beside him, an enthusiastic smile. "You looked beautiful in that light," he said. He turned to Jerry. "How long before we'll know if you got it?"

"I'm heading back to the Bureau now. I'll hit the lab, develop the film, and we should know in a few hours."

At 9:30 that night, Norm got a call from Don Payne. "We got the shot, Norm, and it's fantastic. I think this will go out as soon as you approve it.

"A Vison Over Vegas" was eventually dispatched via the Bureau to every news outlet in the U.S., plus some overseas. To this day, it's considered one of the iconic photographs out of hundreds of thousands shot over the years by some of the best photographers in the world working at the News Bureau at the time.

Lorraine married fellow entertainer Charles "Blackie" Hunt and continued her singing career, performing for the opening of the Landmark Hotel-Casino in 1969. Following her successful show-business career, Lorraine Perry Hunt graduated from songstress to politician. She was elected to the Clark County Commission in 1994; as a commissioner, she served as the first woman Chairperson of the Las Vegas Convention and Visitors Authority (LVCVA), Vice-Chair of the University Medical

Center (UMC), and Trustee on the McCarran International Airport Board of Trustees. In 1998, she was elected Lieutenant Governor of Nevada, then was re-elected in 2002.

During her second term, she and her family opened the now-famous Bootlegger Italian Bistro on Las Vegas Boulevard S., where it still stands today and is a testament to her family's rich heritage of fine Italian dining. On any given evening, she and her present husband, singer and radio personality Dennis Bono, can be found performing at the restaurant.

"Once a singer, always a singer," Lorraine says, standing behind the microphone. Although decades have passed since she graced the world with "A Vision over Vegas," show business is still in her blood.

****

Racing for Recognition

Competition among downtown and Strip casinos escalated during the '60s and downtown casino executives endeavored to create new events that would draw gamblers away from the tonier resorts down on Las Vegas Blvd. and into Fremont Street casinos.

Norm's publicity prowess at the Mint became evident shortly after he was hired. In 1967, he organized an off-road dune-buggy race to promote the Mint's annual deer-hunting contest. LeRoy Wickham and John Sexton, driving two dune buggies and accompanied by one News Bureau photographer, embarked on the off-road run from Las Vegas to the Sahara Tahoe, sister hotel-casino of the Mint. The adventure lasted six days and garnered international press coverage.

The success of the run prompted Norm, also an avid racer, to approach the Mint's vice president and general manager Bill Bennett. Norm believed a larger, more organized race would be a great hotel promotion. Bennett gave Norm the go-ahead and in 1968, Norm organized the first-ever "Mint 400 Off-Road Rally," an off-road run through the desert, from Las Vegas to Beatty, Nevada, and back.

Pulling off the race required some serious groundwork. At first, the Bureau of Land Management refused to allow the race to be run on BLM land. Norm contacted Howard Cannon, who represented Nevada in the U.S. Senate from 1959 to 1983; Cannon convinced the BLM to allow the race. At that time, the Mint 400 was the largest off-road race in the country.

Norm had started racing at the tender age of 14, while living in California. He spent years making friends in racing circles, so to improve the disappointingly small number of entries that were coming in, Norm called his friend, NASCAR driver Mel Larson, in Phoenix and coerced him into participating. Norm then called Lee Iacocca at Ford (the man who was best known for spearheading the development of the Ford Mustang and Pinto and later saved Chrysler) and asked him to donate a vehicle for racing legend Parnelli Jones to race. When Iacocca agreed to provide a Bronco for Parnelli, Norm called Parnelli, his friend from the early days of racing, and coerced him to enter the race as well. It took a bit of bribery.

"Iacocca has agreed to supply a Bronco for you to race and the Mint will give you a thousand dollars cash, whether you win or not. We'll also comp everything during your stay," Norm said, "and take care of your whole crew as well."

Jones had won the Indianapolis 500 in 1963 and once his entry was announced, it opened the floodgates. In total, 109 cars and motorcycles entered the race and, as Norm said, "A dust bowl of chaos ensued."

Joe O'Rayeh, the Mint keno manager, was put in charge of the Beatty checkpoint and fuel stop (a 76 gas station), tasked with recording the racers and their times. But no race of the magnitude of the Mint 400 had ever been held in America and the initial estimates for the first racers to arrive in Beatty were late by nearly 30 minutes. By the time O'Rayeh, dressed in a business suit and alligator shoes, arrived in Beatty, he was enveloped in the massive cloud of dust created by three motorcycles and a pair of cars that had already been fueled and were barreling through the rough desert terrain back to Las Vegas.

After the race, O'Rayeh returned to Las Vegas, covered from head to toe in powder and grime. "Thank God the gas station attendant recorded those first numbers and times," he stated, as he turned in his checkpoint stats. Joe ended up throwing away the suit and shoes after the race.

So many racers were unprepared for the terrain conditions that the route was soon littered with disabled vehicles. Casino executives were furious over the mishaps that plagued the race and the event seemed doomed. But the Mint 400 was saved by Earl Thompson, president of the Sahara Hotel-Casino, who was participating in the race. Although he, along with many other sandblasted racers, had broken down in the desert, when he and his navigator finally arrived at the finish line, covered in dust, Thompson walked up to Norm and said, "This is the greatest goddamned thing I've ever seen!"

Thompson's enthusiasm changed corporate minds. It didn't hurt that the activity surrounding the race was highly publicized and the event was even dubbed "The Great American Desert Race." Race teams and off-road enthusiasts nationwide embraced the 400 and the endurance race became famous overnight. Hosting the event resulted in a packed Mint Hotel, with racing enthusiasts from across the country filling the property to capacity and increasing gambling revenue in the casino by the hundreds of thousands.

Journalist and author Hunter S. Thompson covered the race in 1971, immortalizing it in his scathing satirical novel about the American Dream, *Fear and Loathing in Las Vegas*. In the novel, writing as the character Raoul Duke, Thompson said of the race: "In some circles, the Mint 400 is a far, far better thing than the Super Bowl, the Kentucky Derby and the Lower Oakland Roller Derby Finals all rolled into one. This race attracts a very special breed."

And a rare and colorful breed it was, launching the Mint, and Las Vegas, into the limelight in racing circles for decades to come. On the other hand, in contrast to the new-era casinos being constructed on the Strip, the event only reinforced the reputations of the downtown casinos as aging venues for rough-and-tough gamblers. Cowboys will be cowboys, whether they're riding horses or off-road buggies, and the Mint wasn't immune to the occasional barroom brawl.

As hotel manager of the Mint, when a problem came up that required his attention, Curt Thompson handled it. And when security came to him with any problem, large or small, that upset hotel guests, he handled it personally.

One morning, security reported a problem that set Curt off, his executive guns blazing.

****

Curt, Kent, and Country

"Let's get to the bottom of this." Curt watched as Bill, head of Mint security, pounded on the door of room 522. When there was no answer, Curt signaled for him to pound again. "You say the racket came from this room?" he asked over the booming sound of the guard's fist on the hotel-room door.

"Yeah, we got complaints from guests last night about loud music coming from this room. We called up, but got no response, so we came up to see what was going on. A group of guys were inside, drinking and playing music."

"What time was it?"

"Late. After 3 a.m. We gave them a warning and they promised to quiet down. We didn't know about the phone, though, until this morning." Bill stopped pounding on the door and waited. Still no answer.

"Fine," Curt said. "If he's not going to answer, we're going in." He pulled his pass key out of his pocket and slid it in the door's lock. "Hotel manager. Coming in," he shouted, turning the key and pushing the door open. He gestured for Bill to enter first, then followed behind.

Once inside, they discovered a long-haired, partially dressed man sleeping on the bed.

"What a mess," Curt said, looking around in disgust. Empty liquor and beer bottles and pizza boxes lay strewn on table tops and the floor. In the corner were several guitars and a full drum set.

"Wake this guy up, Bill."

Bill leaned his huge frame over the man, placed his hands on the man's shoulders, and shook. Hard.

The man stirred and looked up at the security guard towering over him. "What the hell is going on? What are you doing in my room?" he said, pushing the guard away.

Bill backed up and allowed Curt to step forward.

"I'm the hotel manager. You got a visit from security last night over a noise complaint."

"Yeah, my band and I were hanging out. I guess we got a little loud. We quieted down. What's the problem?"

Curt scowled at the man. "The problem is someone threw a phone out the window of this hotel room last night." He pointed to the broken window adjacent the bed. "Was that you?"

"Yeah, I did it. Damned thing kept ringing and ringing. We were rehearsing for our gig across the street at the Nugget and it just wouldn't stop." The man shrugged, sat up in the bed, and reached for a cigarette pack sitting behind an ashtray overloaded with butts, an empty bottle of Jim Beam beside it. "What's the big deal?"

Curt eyed the empty bottle and his blood started to boil. "You've made a mess and done damage to this room. You had no business playing loud music at all hours of the night and disturbing our guests."

"It was just music." The man lit a cigarette. "We had to rehearse somewhere."

Curt exploded. "Well, you can rehearse at the Nugget. You're not staying here any longer. I'm throwing you out of this hotel." Curt turned to Bill. "Assist this gentleman, *and* his band, from the hotel. I want them out. Now."

The young man and his band were promptly removed from the premises.

Curt had no idea who he was, or how famous he would become.

Meanwhile, the sign business was booming in Las Vegas and Ad-Art Sign Company had a full plate, designing and erecting new signs. Sign-maintenance contracts with hotels and businesses often proved to be lucrative on the long-term basis and were highly sought after as well.

Dan O'Leary, vice-president and sales manager for Ad-Art, had just made a pitch to Charley Smith, owner of the Golden Nugget, for a new exterior sign. He walked into the Ad-Art office in the company's plant on Oquendo Road in a bad mood.

Kent looked up from his office desk. "How'd it go?"

"My pitch tanked," Dan replied in a grumble. "Smith says he'll never change the existing sign. All the man did during the meeting was complain about the company that's servicing his interior casino signs."

"Really?" Kent said. "Maybe I should make a pitch for a maintenance contract."

"Hell, give it a shot. You might have better luck than I did." Dan waved a dismissive hand in the air and sat down at his desk.

Kent called the Nugget and made an appointment to see Charley. The meeting was scheduled for 10:30 on the same morning Curt threw the band out of the Mint. (Although they didn't realize it at the time, the events of that morning would be the first time Curt and Kent's paths would cross. Not until years later did they learn how.)

Kent walked into the lounge of the Golden Nugget at 10 a.m., thirty minutes before his scheduled appointment. He headed for the bar to order a coffee and noticed a young man sitting at the piano, absently running his fingers over the ivories and humming to himself.

"That sounds familiar," Kent said as he approached the young man.

The man looked up over his shoulder at the tall stranger behind him. "It's a little tune I love called 'Stardust.'" His voice was raspy and he spoke with a Southern drawl.

Kent nodded. He knew the tune well. Hoagy Carmichael, his uncle twice removed, had written it. "Kind of early to be in here playing. Are you in the band that's gigging here at night?"

The man sighed. "Yeah, but our days in Vegas are numbered. We just got thrown out of our rooms at the Mint. We'll have to sleep in our cars if we want to finish this gig." He resumed playing the piano.

"Why'd you get kicked out?"

The man's fingers traveled with ease over the piano keys. He explained about the noise and the phone the night before. "I guess we got a little loud. Security came up and told us to pipe down."

"Did you?"

"Well, we tried, but this morning the hotel's general manager came up to the room. He got hot pretty quick. I have to admit, the room was kind of a mess."

He chuckled to himself and played a comical riff on the piano. "The damn phone just kept ringing and ringing. Anyway, the guy this morning said I could've hurt somebody, pitching it out the window and all. He threw us all out."

Kent smiled. It wasn't hard to see how a guest tossing a phone through the window of the hotel might upset management. And musicians were notorious for trashing hotel rooms. "Sounds like it was quite a night."

"Yeah, we had a lot to drink. I guess we deserved it." He closed the lid over the keyboard.

There was something charismatic about the young musician and Kent decided to try to help. He pulled up a chair beside the piano bench and sat down. "I used to work at the Horseshoe. I could call my old boss over there. I might be able to hook you up with some rooms."

"That'd be right neighborly of you." The man pointed to a large sign at the lounge entrance. It featured a blown-up photo advertising his band. "We've got another week to go. We could sure use a place to stay, if you can manage it."

"I've got an appointment here in the hotel in a few minutes. I'll walk over to the Horseshoe after I'm done and see what I can do. Will you be here awhile?"

"Got nowhere else to go," he replied. "The band's having breakfast in the coffee shop. They'll be showing up here soon. We'll just hang out and wait for you." He extended his hand to Kent.

The two men shook hands. "My name's Kent, by the way."

The man smiled. "I sure appreciate your help. We were lucky to get this gig in the first place, considering the music we play." He sighed and shook his head. "But we keep playing. I just know someday country music will catch on. The name's Willie. Willie Nelson. It's a pleasure to meet you."

Some years later, Curt Thompson was now executive VP at the Frontier. Kent was managing Ad-Art and supervising the construction of the new Frontier pylon. The two men were having lunch and discussing progress on the sign when conversation shifted to entertainment on the Strip.

"Headliners sure have changed over the years," Kent said. "Caesars Palace just booked a country act to follow Diana Ross. I know the guy. I met him back at the Nugget years ago."

Curt nearly choked on his coffee when he heard the comment. "Are you talking about Willie Nelson?" He stifled a laugh. "I know him, too, from back when I was hotel manager of the Mint. He and his band were playing at the

Nugget across the street and had rooms at the Mint. I had to throw him and his whole band out of the hotel for trashing the place." He shook his head. "And look at Willie now. Who knew he'd become such a huge star?"

"That was you?" Kent asked. "It's a small world."

"What do you mean?"

"I'm the guy who got Willie and his band a place to stay when you threw them out of your hotel."

Curt sighed. "Well, I guess he can stay wherever he likes these days."

"Yeah," Kent said. "He told me he knew that someday country music would catch on. Turns out, he was right."

6

Jerry Builds a Club

Las Vegas has long been called "Sin City," internationally recognized as one of the world's most enticing adult playgrounds, from the blissfully innocent to the downright degenerate. Through the decades, the city has gladly provided anything that can be imagined and desired. In Las Vegas, money doesn't just talk, it shouts.

But beyond the glitter, glamour, and decadence of the Las Vegas tourist corridor, with its stories of strong-armed mobsters and lascivious call girls, every era flourished with behind-the-scenes acts of philanthropy. Local business owners joined forces with casino owners, initiating programs to improve the lives of Las Vegans. With his arrival in Las Vegas in 1965, Gerald "Jerry" Gillock would become one of those men. He was about to build something special.

****

All for the Kids

The idea to create the Boys Club of Clark County was the brainchild of a group of Vegas businessmen. Casino owners Sam Boyd and Jackie Gaughan, along with Jim Cashman Jr., owner of Cashman Cadillac, joined forces with Walt Geary and Frank Rogers, the two heads of the local phone company, to initiate the program.

"We need to do something for the disadvantaged kids whose parents have a hard time making a living in our community," Gaughan said as the men sat in his El Cortez coffee shop, discussing potential projects. This town's growing like crazy and a club for our underprivileged youth is long overdue. These kids need a facility that offers them a safe place to play, learn, and grow."

The others agreed and the wheels started turning. A Boys Club of America was the perfect vehicle, an organization all about helping the youth of America.

To ensure the success of the project, the group contacted the leaders of the national Boys Club organization and Jerry Gillock was called in to oversee the Las Vegas project.

Jerry had recently graduated from college in Garden Grove, California. As the recipient of a hardship scholarship awarded by the Boys Club of America, upon graduation he was required to work for the Boys Club for a period of three years. He relocated to Las Vegas and began laying the foundation for the city's first club.

Initially, the youth program was set up in the basement of the Silver Nugget Casino in North Las Vegas, but within a year, the sponsors had successfully raised $100,000 and acquired a matching grant from a local philanthropist. The funds made it possible for Jerry, now acting as the program's executive director, to oversee the construction of the first facility-based Boys Club in Las Vegas.

This was the first imprint Jerry would make on the city. In the coming years, he went on to receive a law degree, become an acclaimed attorney, and litigate high-profile cases involving major Las Vegas casinos. But for the moment, he was building a youth center.

The controversy over the club's location began immediately.

"These kids have nothing," Jerry said, defending the decision to build in a location on East Carey in North Las Vegas, an area considered by many to be the wrong side of the tracks. "We need to get them off the streets after school. They need a supervised program of athletics and social activities. The North Las Vegas kids are the ones who need it most," he insisted. Jerry and the rest of the board countered criticism over the location with resolve and won. The club was completed and hundreds of kids immediately benefited.

****

It's a Small World

By 1966, the basketball program at the Boys Club had grown extensively since the rec center opened its doors. Tennis shoes squeaked against the basketball floor as agile youths ran up and down the court, effortlessly dunking and rebounding balls. The sounds of their laughter combined with the thumping of dribbling basketballs and echoed off the walls.

Two young boys, Jimmy and Michael, chatted while waiting for their turn on the court. "I can't believe we're really going to meet an astronaut," Jimmy said as he and Michael passed a basketball back and forth.

"Me either," Michael replied. "Gus Grissom, at our club. He's famous."

Lieutenant Colonel Virgil "Gus" Grissom had been part of the U.S. manned space program since it began in 1959. He was selected as one of NASA's original seven Mercury astronauts and his second space flight on Gemini III earned him the distinction of being the first man to fly in space twice, completing a successful three-orbit mission on March 23, 1965. He was an American hero. And now he was coming to visit the club.

"My mom didn't believe it either at first," Jimmy said. "She said important men like astronauts don't have time for kids from neighborhoods like ours."

"I bet she was surprised when she found out it was true," Jimmy said, grinning. "A real-live astronaut. I'm sure glad my mom let me join this club. She said I'd be safe here after school until she got home from work."

"Yeah, mine, too. She signed me up as soon as she heard the club was opening."

The sudden shrill blast of a whistle was followed by the booming voice of the basketball coach. "Group B, off the court. Group C, you're up. Ten-minute warm up."

"I think maybe I'd like to be an astronaut when I grow up," Michael said, playfully nudging Jimmy as they ran onto the court.

"Yeah, like that'll ever happen," Jimmy said, slipping past Michael and stealing the basketball from his friend's grasp. "But tell you what, first one to make a basket gets to shake the astronaut's hand."

Both boys giggled. They loved basketball. And they loved the club.

On the day Gus Grissom was scheduled to visit, the club was packed to capacity. "I see a limo pulling up," Jimmy said, craning his neck to look outside.

The kids sitting near the window clamored to their feet and rushed over to get a better look.

"Calm down, everyone," a flustered staff member called out to the crowd of unruly onlookers as they jostled for position and pressed their noses up against the windowpane.

"Take your seats," the club's director hollered out. "Mr. Grissom's arrived. Let's show him how we welcome guests to our club."

The kids returned to their seats, their eyes glued to the door. When it swung open and Gus Grissom entered, flanked by two of Metro's finest and an entourage of politicians and local businessmen, the room was quiet enough to hear the proverbial pin drop.

The club's director approached the podium. "We are honored today to have our own U.S. Senator Howard Cannon in attendance, along with North Las Vegas Mayor William Taylor." He gestured to the men seated behind him.

The room filled with polite applause as the senator and mayor were introduced, but when the club director introduced Gus Grissom, the room exploded in applause and cheers.

Gus stood behind the podium. He gestured for the kids to quiet down and began his speech. He spoke of the years of preparation leading up to the flight, of the study, training, and dedication required to accomplish the goal of going into space. When he asked for questions from the audience, dozens of hands sprung up.

Michael jumped up, waving his hand back and forth. "Me!" he said, shouting at the top of his lungs. "I have a question."

"That's the spirit," Gus said, pointing at Michael. "What's your question?"

Michael's eyes were as big as saucers as he addressed the larger-than-life hero standing before him. "What's it like to be in space? To see the Earth from the stars?"

"What's your name, young man?" Gus asked.

"It's Michael," he replied.

Gus placed both hands on the podium and looked out over the crowd of eager young faces. He chose his words with care. "Well, Michael, from Space, the world looks small. So never hesitate and think it's too big for you to make a difference. You can do anything you set your mind to. Be strong."

The afternoon came to an end. Gus Grissom left the Boys Club, but not before he and Senator Cannon shook hands with every single boy there.

"This was so great," Michael whispered to Jimmy as the two boys watched Gus Grissom's limo drive away. "Did you hear what Astronaut Grissom said? I can do anything I set my mind to. I'm definitely going to be an astronaut when I grow up."

(In 1990, the Boys Clubs expanded to include girls, becoming the Boys & Girls Clubs of Clark County. In addition, in November of 2013, the Boys & Girls Clubs of Henderson and Boys and Girls Clubs of Las Vegas merged to form the Boys & Girls Clubs of Southern Nevada.)

7

The Bank Vault

To this day, many people have a common misconception about Las Vegas. The myth holds that Sin City is limited to a long stretch of casinos and tourist attractions, devoid of church and community, in an atmosphere where normal suburban American life is nonexistent.

Nothing could be further from the truth. As the city continued to grow and expand, homes were built to accommodate the myriad families moving to southern Nevada to pursue employment.

In addition to dealers, cocktail waitresses, hotel workers, and casino managers, new non-casino jobs were abundant. From grocery stores to cab companies, furniture stores to car dealerships, Las Vegas was becoming a real city. As businesses in every walk of life opened their doors, it seemed opportunities were behind every door.

One such business, Nevada State Bank, celebrated its grand opening and ribbon cutting on January 8, 1960, at its headquarters at Fourth and Carson streets downtown. Some years later, a mishap occurred at the bank, and the police were called in to help. But it was a reluctant hero with an unusual set of skills who stepped in to save the day.

****

"Who the hell locked the vault?" John Burton, the Nevada State Bank main-branch manager demanded as he pulled on the huge steel door. He turned away, pushed open the double doors separating the area from the bank lobby, and walked toward the security guard standing at the bank entrance. It was 11:30 on a Thursday morning and the bank was open and crowded. He made his way past customers at tellers' windows and continued along the queue of waiting patrons. He reached the front of the bank and addressed the security guard. "Did you lock the vault, Doug?"

"No," the guard replied. "It should be closed, but not locked."

"Well, some idiot's locked it," Burton said, his tone a mixture of concern and frustration. "I've looked all over for the auditor and I think he may be trapped in there. We've got to do something."

Doug looked around to see curious onlookers reacting to their conversation. "We'd better keep our voices down," he whispered.

Burton scanned the lobby. He eyed nervous tellers glancing at him with apprehension from behind their stations. Burton was a big man, five-ten and more than 250 pounds. He had a short temper and little patience when it came to problems at the bank.

At the harsh sound of his boss's voice, Brian Jamison, the assistant bank manager, appeared from his office in the front left corner of the bank lobby. "What's going on? Do we have a problem?"

Burton glared at him. "Yes. Come with me."

Brian rushed to join the manager. They walked from the front of the bank back to the double doors separating the vault from the lobby area. Brian's spare tire of body fat jiggled like a bowl of Jell-O under his open suit jacket as he hustled to keep up with his boss.

Burton pulled the two doors open and nodded in the direction of the vault. "This is serious, Brian," the manager said as the two men entered the back area housing the vault and safety deposit boxes. "Check with all the tellers. See if anyone knows anything."

Jamison scurried off. A few minutes later, he returned. "Nobody's seen him, but I was in the vault with him a little before ten, so it had to happen after that." Jamison ran his thumb along his fingers, counting. A look of panic covered his face. "He'll be stuck in there for hours."

The two men entered Burton's office. Burton slammed the door behind them and reached for the Rolodex on his desk. He dialed the main police station downtown.

"Las Vegas Police Department."

"This is John Burton, bank manager at Nevada State Bank on Fourth and Carson. We've got a man locked in our vault. I need assistance getting him out."

"Please hold."

Burton stood beside his desk, nervously tapping his free hand on the desktop.

A moment later, the police chief was on the line. "Hello, this is Police Chief Witcher. You've got a man locked in your vault? Don't you have an override? I mean, isn't there any way to trip the lock?"

"I'm afraid not," the bank manager replied. He explained how the bank kept the vault closed and unlocked during banking hours, but someone had accidentally turned the vault wheel and engaged the 12-hour timer. "There's nothing we can do to get it open until the timer disengages."

"Can't you just wait?"

"Well, I'm afraid that creates a problem for the man locked inside," Burton said.

"Why?"

"The vault doesn't have a separate ventilation system. The guy could suffocate in there if we don't get him out."

The police chief was a man who took pride in solving problems. "I have an idea," he said. "Hang on a minute."

"Great, thanks." Burton looked over at Jamison. He nodded up and down and silently mouthed a hopeful, "OK."

A few minutes later, the police chief returned to the phone. "I know a guy who can help you. I'm dispatching two officers down to a plant on Oquendo Road to find him, and two more officers to the bank. Hang tight." He hung up.

****

The Safe Cracker

Shortly after receiving their orders, two police officers arrived at the Ad-Art sign plant on Oquendo Road. All the work crews hanging and servicing signs had already been dispatched to their designated sites and the place was quiet. The officers entered the front offices of the plant and approached Dindy Clark, a woman in her mid-20s, sitting behind a reception desk. She was known as much for her dynamite legs as her unique first name.

"We're looking for Dick Kline. Is he here?" one of the officers asked.

"I don't know, officer. But Mr. Carmichael, the manager, is here. He would know." She buzzed Kent to announce the officers' arrival, then directed them to a back office.

Kent was sitting at a desk working on a sign estimate when the officers entered. He looked up. One officer stood at six feet and had the physical appearance of a professional linebacker. His fellow officer, although not quite so tall, was equally muscular.

"We're looking for Dick Kline. We know he works here."

Although Dick was one of many men working for Ad-Art, building and erecting signs, he had, bar none, the most colorful past. He was 50 years old—long, lean, three-quarters Cherokee, and in his day a master thief. It was a lucrative occupation that suited him well until he got caught breaking into a bank vault and ended up doing time up at California Institution for Men in Chino, near Riverside in southern California. When he got out, he went straight. Kent had taken a chance hiring him as a sign hanger, and the two men had grown close.

Kent's voice remained calm, but he felt a twinge of anxiety over the thought of two police officers looking for Dick. "Why are you looking for him?"

The answer was abrupt. "We just need him. Is he here?"

"He's onsite working one of the jobs on the Strip. I'll go out into the warehouse and find out which one. Excuse me for a minute." Kent inched his way around the two officers and headed toward the door for the main warehouse.

"We'll be here. Don't be long," one of the officers grunted.

Kent entered the warehouse and approached a maintenance worker sweeping the warehouse floor. "Ralph, where's Dick Kline working today?"

"He's at the Thunderbird, boss, with Andy and Ferrill. They left hours ago. They'll be there working on the pylon at the front of the property all day. Why?"

Kent looked behind him. The officers had remained in his office, out of earshot. "Listen, Ralph. Get in your truck. Go over there and warn Dick that two cops are looking for him. They won't tell me why they want him and I don't like their attitude. We can at least give him a head's-up."

Ralph nodded. "OK, boss. I'll let him know."

"Thanks, Ralph. Just let him know I had no choice but to tell the cops where he is. Get going."

Ralph winked and headed for his truck.

Kent stayed in the warehouse, stalling for time. After a few minutes, he returned to his office to face the officers.

"Well, that took a while. Where is he?" the bigger officer barked, locking his thumbs in his belt loops.

Kent stalled a bit longer. "No one in the warehouse knows, but I can check the work manifest and see where he might be." He reached for a work sheet on his desk.

"Hurry up," the officer said, glaring at him. "We need this guy now."

Kent flipped a couple of pages on a ledger and ran his finger down the column. "Ah, here he is. He's on the work detail servicing the Thunderbird sign. You should find him out front of the Thunderbird, down on—"

"We know where it is. Are you sure he's there?"

"He should be. He's on the work manifest along with the rest of the crew. My two main guys, Andy Lodewyck and Ferrill Rushton, are there. Andy's a lean, wiry guy, about five-nine, brown hair. Ferrill's got red hair. One of them can point Dick out to you."

The two officers left the office and sped off in their squad car, spraying gravel in the lot.

Kent stood beside Dindy's desk and watched out the front window as the officers disappeared in a cloud of dust. "Dindy, I'll be over at the Thunderbird if anyone needs me." He hurried to the parking lot behind the shop, got in his work truck, pulled out of the lot, and headed for the Thunderbird.

The two officers were talking to Andy at the base of the Thunderbird sign when Kent arrived. He parked and approached the group. "Everything all right here?"

"Hey, Kent. I was just telling these officers that Dick's not here. He was a minute ago." Andy's Southern drawl masked the amusement showing in his eyes. "He must've taken a break. You know how these guys can wander off sometimes," he said, grinning.

"It's not funny, pal," one officer said. He looked around at the group of brawny men working on the sign. The temperature out in the sun had already skyrocketed to a sizzling 105 degrees. Their T-shirts were soaked in sweat and their faces and arms were deeply tanned. "Listen, we need to find this guy."

Kent intervened. "Look, I don't want any trouble on the site. Why do you need him?"

"It's none of your damned business," the taller officer barked.

"Wait a minute," the second officer interrupted. He placed his huge hand on his fellow officer's arm. "Take it easy. These men are working hard out here in the hot sun. Nothing good can come from insulting their boss." He pushed past the officer to face Kent. "Here's the deal," he began, "we've got a guy locked in a vault downtown at Nevada State Bank."

The work crew standing nearby burst into spontaneous laughter.

"A VIP locked in a bank vault?" One crew member elbowed a fellow worker. "No wonder they need Dick."

"Are you sure Dick isn't in trouble?" Kent asked. "He's a good worker. Unless he's done something wrong, he needs to stay on the job."

"He's not in trouble. The air supply in the vault could run out for the guy stuck inside. We have to get the door open and the chief needs Mr. Kline's expertise," he said, raising his hands and emphasizing the word "expertise" with air quotes.

The work crew howled when they heard the officer's statement.

"That's hilarious," Ferrill said. "Two cops need Dick to do precisely what Dick isn't supposed to be doing."

"Cool it, guys. This doesn't involve you." Kent tossed his head in the direction of the pylon. "Get back to work."

The men dispersed, still chuckling.

"Can I talk to you for a minute, boss?" Andy whispered. He pulled Kent away from the officers' earshot and tossed his head to his left. "I think I know where Dick might be." He jutted his chin toward a café nearby.

Kent glanced in the direction of the nod. He spotted Ralph's work truck parked in the parking lot across the street in front of the Algiers coffee shop.

"He's with Ralph," Andy said. "No way Dick was going to offer himself up to the police."

"What's he saying?" one of the officers said. "Does he know where Kline is?"

"No," Kent lied. "But I might. Let me find Dick and bring him to you." He paused. "Dick trusts me. I'll locate him and bring him to the bank myself."

The officers reluctantly agreed. "Well, if he's not here, he's not here," the friendlier officer said.

The unfriendly one leaned in and poked his forefinger on Kent's chest. "Just find Kline. And do it quick."

Andy and Kent watched as the officers returned to their squad car and peeled off up the Strip toward the bank.

Once they were out of sight, Kent walked across the street to the coffee shop. He opened the door to the sound of clanging slot machines lined up against the wall. He rounded the row of machines and passed the long breakfast counter.

Ralph and Dick were sitting at a table by the window, drinking coffee. From where they sat, they'd had a bird's-eye view of the activity taking place under the pylon. They acknowledged Kent as he approached.

"Hi, boss." Dick saluted him with smile and a casual flick of his wrist. "What's going on?"

Kent sat down.

The smile on Dick's face disappeared when Kent explained why the cops were looking for him. "The vault's on a time lock. Can you open it?"

Ralph gave Dick a playful punch on the shoulder. "A bank job. Just your cup of tea."

Dick scanned the coffee shop for patrons within earshot. The coast was clear. Nobody beyond their table could hear him. He shot Ralph a dirty look, then leaned in toward Kent. "There isn't a vault I can't open, but I sure as hell don't want to go back to jail. You know I'm not supposed to be anywhere near a safe, much less a vault like the one in that bank."

"It's not a problem, Dick. If you can get the vault open and get this guy out, no one will care how you did it," Kent replied.

"Do I have to, boss? I mean, really. Me and cops, in a bank?" There was fear in his eyes. "I don't like it."

"I don't think you have much of a choice." Kent gave him a reassuring pat on the shoulder. "It might be a nice gesture of good will," he let out a small laugh, "considering your past experience with the law."

A tiny smile appeared on Dick's face. "I guess it might be a challenge."

"Come on, I'll take you myself," Kent said. "It'll be fun."

"Fun, right, sure. Me and cops in a bank at the same time." Dick rose from the table and stretched his arms over his head, wiggling his fingers like he was warming up to play a piano. "I'll need my tool box from Ralph's truck. I've still got some special tools I made up for this kind of thing." His tiny smile had grown. It lit up his tanned leathery face. "Maybe you're right. It'll be fun to crack open a safe. It's been way too long."

Kent and Dick arrived at the bank a little after 1 p.m. At this point the auditor had been locked inside the vault for more than two hours. The clock was ticking.

The activity inside the bank appeared normal, except for a group of police officers gathered in front of the doors leading to the vault area.

Dick cringed at the sight of them. He followed behind Kent. "Whose bright idea was this, anyway?" he muttered as they approached the officers.

"Actually, it was mine." Police Chief Witcher stepped forward. His tone was warm. Over the years, Dick had become something of a legend down at the precinct. Something about his personality was downright appealing, safecracker or not. "I hear you've been behaving yourself," he said. "I hope we'll be able to put your talents to good use today."

Dick grunted. "Yeah, well, I'm not so sure, seeing as how I don't crack safes anymore." He emphasized the last four words.

Bank manager Burton walked up to Dick with the reluctance of a kitten afraid of its own shadow. His brash demeanor had wilted away when the police chief told him a former bank robber was being dispatched to assist. "My name's John Burton. I'm the bank manager. So, can you do it?" He eyed Dick with apprehension, leaning toward fear.

Dick scrutinized the fat man in the expensive business suit. His jet-black eyes locked onto Burton's. He answered in a deep monotone, "I have to see the vault."

Burton looked at the police chief, who nodded an OK. Then he turned to Dick. "This way." He led Dick through the double doors to the vault, two police officers following close behind.

Dick glanced at the vault, then said, "I want to talk to Kent. Alone."

Burton gave the officers a puzzled look. They just shrugged. "Give the guy what he wants," one of the officers said.

Burton left to retrieve Kent from the lobby while the two officers remained at Dick's side.

"We need to talk." Dick pulled Kent around the corner into the adjacent hall leading to the employee entrance in back. He leaned in and spoke softly. "I can open this vault. It's a piece of cake and I'll do it, for you. But how I do it has to stay between the two of us. No one else gets near us, understand?"

"OK, Dick, that's great. Do you want to give them the news?"

"Hell, no. It just isn't natural buddying up with bankers or cops." Dick gave him a pleading look. "You can talk for me. OK?"

Kent nodded. "What do you want me to say?"

"Just tell them I can do it, but I want some guarantees. I walk out of here when it's done. And remember, just us two in here and nobody else. Got it?"

"No problem, Dick, if that's what you want."

"I need my tool box," Dick said. "Can you get it for me?"

"Sure thing," Kent replied, grinning to himself at how the tables had turned and now he was working for Dick.

The police chief accompanied Kent to his truck.

"How'd you get him to agree to come with you?" he asked. "Dick isn't exactly the trusting type."

Kent reached for his keys and opened the truck's passenger door. "It wasn't hard. When he first came to work for me, he was no different from many of the other men I employ. They're a rough bunch, but underneath, given a chance, most of them are good guys." He grabbed the tool box. "Dick and I hit it off right away. He's one of us now and sign men look out for each other. It's a brotherhood."

"Yeah, we've got that on the force, too," Witcher said.

The two men returned to the bank. They found Dick standing by the wall housing the control panel. The bank manager stood a few yards away from Dick, flanked by two officers.

Kent set the tool box on the floor in front of Dick.

The police chief gave it a tap with the toe of his shoe. "Here it is. Now what?"

"Now everybody leaves us alone," Kent said, using his assertive sign-boss tone.

Dick kneeled down and put his hand on the top of his tool box. He looked at the police chief and waited.

Police Chief Witcher gave him a stern look. "All right, but we'll be just around the corner at the vault entrance. No one comes in or out." He directed the bank manager and the two officers to leave the area. "Like I said," he turned back to give Dick another look as he walked away, "we'll be just around the corner."

Once everyone had left the corridor, Dick pointed to a panel on the wall beside them. "That's the control panel. Somewhere inside, there's a time-lock mechanism. That's where we start." He opened his tool box. "We need to remove the security panel with a special screw gun. I just happen to have one."

Dick's adrenaline was pumping as he retrieved the screw gun from his toolbox. It had been a long time since he'd used his special tools.

He carefully began removing the custom-made stainless-steel screws on the face of the panel. "Supposedly, these are tamper-proof screws," he said, delivering the comment with smug sarcasm.

As he worked, Dick delivered a master class in safecracking technique. He informed Kent that the screws were manufactured with left-handed threads, cut in a way that made them impossible to remove without the specially designed tool. Dick flashed a mischievous grin as he waved the screw gun in the air. "Just like this one here that I made myself. It took me a long time to machine this puppy."

Ten minutes passed. After he'd successfully removed 24 screws from the panel, Dick pulled two suction cups from his toolbox, similar to the type used by glass installers. He placed them on the panel and moved it up and slightly to the right. When he heard a click, he pulled the panel toward him, exposing the electrical mechanisms inside.

He handed Kent the panel cover. "Set it down and be sure to keep the top section up."

"Yes, sir, Mr. Kline." Kent set the panel cover down.

"Now, get me my voltage meter. It's in a black-leather case at the bottom of my tool box."

Kent retrieved the meter and handed it to Dick, who proceeded to plug in two wires with electrical probes onto the face of the meter, one red and one black.

"Hold the meter for me," Dick said. He began scanning the panel and testing the neatly arranged wires for voltage.

"What are you looking for?" Kent asked.

Dick ignored the question. His eyes were locked on the wires. "There they are," he said as he tested two screws on the panel. "Twelve volts DC, the time-lock motor wires. I found those suckers."

Dick freed the two wires. He held them side by side, cautioning Kent as he spoke, "Remember this. The orange and white wire was taken from the left screw; the red and black is off the right."

Kent nodded that he understood.

"Now, I need that battery pack in my tool box."

Kent handed the pack to Dick.

"This battery pack has fourteen nine-volt batteries on a custom rheostat. It's capable of varying voltages, so what we have here is a battery pack capable of a hundred twenty-six volts DC." He paused. "I'm going to hook up this battery pack to the wires we just disconnected from the panel. Watch and learn."

Kent shook his head. "Hey, you're the safecracker. I'm just along for the ride."

Dick attached the two battery-pack wires to the voltage meter. "I'm zeroing out the rheostat." He double-checked to make sure it was cleared of all voltage. When he was confident no voltage was coming from the pack, he hooked the battery wires to the two wires hanging from the panel. "Now, watch this."

He steadily upped the rheostat until it reached full power, sending 126 volts to the time-clock motor.

Dick turned to Kent. "We've just accelerated the speed of the clock."

"Yeah? How much faster?

"Ten times."

Kent laughed. "Making time fly, huh?"

"You bet," Dick replied. "What time is it?"

Kent pulled up his shirt cuff to check his watch. "It's two p.m."

"OK, if the vault got locked after ten a.m. and it's on a twelve-hour time lock, that leaves us a little less than eight hours. It should take around forty minutes or so before the time lock releases."

"Is that it?" Kent asked. "We just wait around for forty minutes and the time lock will release? And then the vault can be opened?"

"Yep, that's all there is to it, but you never saw this. Once the time lock releases, I'll put everything in the panel box back as before." Dick's voice crackled with excitement. He was once again a man in full-on safecracking mode.

"After this guy's out of the vault, someone from the vault company's going to have to come in and reset the timer sequence." His voice quieted. "Kent, I mean it, nobody comes back here except you until we put it back together and I put my tools away."

Kent looked at his friend with awe. "Dick, you're a genius. Who knew something so simple could override the time lock on a million-dollar vault? You might be working as a sign hanger, but hell, you were born to be a safecracker."

"Go out there and tell them it'll take about forty more minutes. Then come back in here and keep me company until the lock releases. Nobody comes in, right?"

"Right."

"No bank manager or police officer can ever see me with these tools."

"Got it." Kent gave Dick two thumbs up and went out to the vault to deliver the news. He returned five minutes later. "Well, they had all kinds of questions, but I just played dumb and told them you were still working back here. They agreed to leave us alone and wait like you said."

As the minutes ticked by, Kent and Dick sat side by side on the tile floor. Dick was busy telling Kent about the progress on the Thunderbird marquee when they heard a loud click. Kent looked at his watch. Dick's calculations were spot on. The time lock released forty-two minutes later, only two minutes off Dick's predicted time.

"I'll be a son of a gun," bank manager Burton said to the police chief at the sound of the lock disengaging. "He did it."

The police chief shook his head. "I have no idea how Kline pulled it off, but I'll be damned if he didn't open that vault. Let's get the auditor out of there."

Bank manager Burton dialed in the code. He turned the wheel and swung open the vault door.

"Thank God," a voice from inside shouted. The auditor, suit jacket and necktie in hand, exited the vault. Beads of sweat had formed on his bald head and his cheeks were flushed. He stopped only inches away from bank manager Burton, and lifted his head to eyeball the man. "I thought I was going to suffocate in there," he said. His tone was a mixture of reprimand and relief. "Who the hell locked me in?"

Dick and Kent remained around the corner by the control panel, listening to the commotion as the bank manager attempted to calm the auditor.

"We did it, Kent," Dick said as he reached for his special tool. "Now hand me one of those screws. Let's get this panel closed up. I want to get the hell out of this bank."

8

Gangland

In the mid-'60s, the mob's reign over Las Vegas began to decline, as corporations took notice of the fortunes being made in the gaming industry. Eager to capitalize on the city's wealth and ongoing potential for more, they began forcing the mob out of Las Vegas, hotel by hotel. Politicians were no longer in the pocket of the Benny Binions and Eddie Torres of Las Vegas. They were now under the thumb of business tycoons with power equaling that of the Chicago Syndicate. They tightened and enforced laws that compelled once-untouchable casino bosses to sell out or face unwanted scrutiny, including possible incarceration.

The takeover slowly transformed Las Vegas, squeezing out aging gangsters and replacing them with corporate bean-counters. While some hangers-on managed to hold on to their properties for a time, the arrival of billionaires like Howard Hughes, Kirk Kerkorian, and Barron Hilton, who had access to a lot more money than the mob, placed inevitable change on the horizon.

Not all who embraced this change were already powerful men.

One young aspiring entrepreneur with dreams of owning his own casino realized that he was a clear underdog in competition against the huge corporate machines. He had no choice but to align himself with old-school strongholds, using his charm to coerce still-powerful Las Vegas casino owners into assisting him. With their help, he began to achieve his goals.

That man was Steve Wynn.

His vision for Las Vegas began in front of the sign in the parking lot of the Frontier Hotel in 1967.

The sun was setting over Red Rock Canyon as Kent Carmichael stepped off the bottom ladder rung and looked up at the Frontier pylon marquee sparkling above his head. The sign comprised three levels. The first rested forty feet above the ground and housed a 20-foot-high reader unit with backlit lettering that advertised amenities at the hotel, such as $9.95 half-rack rib dinners and steak and shrimp specials. A second section, the same size, advertised rooms starting at $44.95, Sunday through Thursday. The third was another 60 feet up to the neon-lit letters spelling out "Frontier." Forty-thousand incandescent lamps formed the Frontier letters, flashing against a background of vertical red neon lines. Finally, towering another 40 feet in the air, a giant "F" rotated between the two lit pylons that supported the marquee. The two pylons curved together, joining in an arch above the "F" 200 feet above the ground.

Ad-Art had recently built the Frontier marquee and held the maintenance contract. Earlier in the evening, when the sign turned on, a circuit blew, darkening one section of the main reader unit. When the call came in about the circuit, Kent answered it. He was about to head back up to double check the circuit breakers when a man approached him.

"Hi, my name's Steve Wynn," the man said. "I'm the new slot and keno manager at the Frontier." He extended his hand to Kent.

As the two men shook hands, Kent observed the young man in front of him. He looked to be in his mid-twenties, with black hair and a tanned face that sported a million-dollar smile. He was wearing a crisp white shirt, black pants, and a name tag that read "Steve."

"I'm Kent Carmichael. What can I do for you?"

Steve explained his fascination with the Frontier sign. He said he was curious about its construction and the details of its component parts. "I've been waiting for you to come down from the sign. I was hoping you might allow me to take a look inside."

The young man looked fit, but his request wasn't just unusual, it was potentially dangerous. Non-sign men were rarely granted access to the interiors of the big signs.

Kent decided to find out more about him. "Tell me about yourself, Steve."

Steve's smile widened as he spoke about his adventures and aspirations. Kent learned that he was an avid snow-skier, which explained his strong physique, and that his father had encouraged him to learn as much as he could about the gaming industry. Steve explained that his dad had run a series of bingo parlors in various states, exposing him to the business at an early age. Steve had even made a small financial investment in the Frontier.

"I'm interested in all aspects of gaming, including signs like this one. It really draws customers into the casino." His eyes shone with the exuberance of an eager student as he spoke about his plans for the future.

The sun was down by the time Steve finished his pitch. Kent could easily see that the kid had it all—looks, charm, and a serious work ethic, Along with irresistible energy and a flair for communication.

Kent looked down at Steve's shoes and saw they were rubber-soled, sensible shoes for climbing. "OK, I'll take you up. Follow me."

Steve followed close behind, climbing the 40-foot vertical ladder enclosed in the sign's right pylon. He made the climb up into the main reader unit with ease.

Kent was an experienced snow-skier and when Steve mentioned that he wanted to helicopter drop into the Bugaboos of Canada and ski down, he realized that if the young man was that good a skier, he must be quite an athlete. There was little doubt he could handle the vertical climb up into the reader unit. How much farther he would want to go remained to be seen.

Once inside the massive unit, Kent explained all the working components and how they were linked to light the reader board.

Steve listened, his eyes scanning the multitude of circuits, wiring, and electronic equipment in the interior of the board.

"The ladder continues up another sixty feet to the neon 'Frontier' lettering. If you're game, we can continue up a little farther."

Steve readily agreed and the two men resumed their climb, with Steve going first and Kent following behind him for safety. Once they reached the top of the reader board, Steve found himself once again climbing inside the narrow pylon. Unaffected by the space constraints, he continued the climb up to the base of the Frontier letters.

The pylon once again opened up into a huge area, 30 feet tall by 100 feet across. The pungent smell permeating the area was a combination of electrical ozone gas from the many transformers and pigeon droppings.

"Amazing," Steve said, wide-eyed, as he stepped off the ladder into the area housing the letters. "This must've been a bearcat to build," he yelled over the noise created by the machines surrounding them.

Kent laughed. "Well, if you like this, climb up to that top hatch. Open it and look up." He pointed up another 30 feet above them to a hatch at the top of the structure. "The Frontier 'F' is rotating another forty feet above that hatch."

Steve didn't hesitate. He grabbed a ladder rung and started the trek up, climbing with speed and agility.

Kent had planned for their climb to end in the lettering. It was a remarkable climb up to the "F," even for a sign man. Steve was proving he was fearless.

Kent followed him up the ladder to the top of the Frontier lettering. Fit or not, Steve had climbed as far as Kent was going to allow. "We'll stop here."

He got no argument from Steve, who'd popped his head out of the hatch opening and wrenched his neck back to see the ladder continuing farther up. "Oh my God, that's *way* up there." He held tight to the ladder rung. "I think I've gone high enough."

Kent followed behind Steve as they descended. Once they were both safely on the ground, Steve looked up at the "F" rotating at the top of the marquee. "How many feet up to the top?"

"From the ground, nearly two hundred," Kent replied. "You made it over three-quarters of the way. Not many men have been up that far."

"Thanks for indulging me. When I get that ski trip organized, I'll give you a call."

Kent reached in his shirt pocket and pulled out his business card. He handed the card to Steve. "I look forward to that, Steve."

Steve put the card in his pocket, and then gestured up at the marquee towering over his head. "I plan on building my own casinos one day and I'll want signs like that." He flashed another million-dollar smile. "And I'll be asking you to build them for me."

As Kent watched Steve sprint back into the casino, he realized he'd met a young man with the determination to accomplish all he would set out to do.

"You'd make one hell of a good sign man," Kent said under his breath as Steve disappeared back into the casino.

But Steve Wynn was destined for bigger things.

****

A Big Idea of Steve's Means Hot Water for Kent

Howard Hughes purchased the Frontier Hotel shortly after Kent's encounter with the young entrepreneur. As Kent later learned, the sale resulted in Wynn losing the 5% business interest he'd purchased in the hotel, via reputed Detroit mobster Anthony Zerilli. With his $75,000 investment in the Frontier gone, Wynn began exploring new ventures of his own.

A few years after the sale of the Frontier, Steve called Kent at Ad-Art. He needed a new sign for his recent purchase of Best Brands Distributing. It wasn't a casino. It was a liquor company. But he still needed a sign.

Kent pulled the company truck to a stop at the Best Brands warehouse on South Arville Street near the Strip and entered the office. Steve's flair for interior design showed in the décor. White, gold, and black were the predominant colors, and the resulting overall effect was elegant modern art deco. The entire office was immaculate.

Steve rose from behind his desk. "Welcome," he said, flashing his signature smile. "Let me show you the brains of this outfit."

Steve led Kent into the Best Brands computer room. At the entranceway, the two men cleaned the bottoms of their shoes by stepping onto a sticky matt that removed dust and any other lingering debris. "This area has to be kept immaculate. All the equipment must be kept sterile." He gestured to an impressive array of floor-to-ceiling islands of reel-to-reel data tape machines blanketing the room. "I've completely modernized my inventory system. Remind you of anything?" he asked, grinning.

Kent looked around the room. "I'm not sure what you mean."

Steve's dark brown eyes twinkled. "This is my version of your Frontier reader board. It's not quite as high up, but the equipment's just as impressive."

Kent laughed out loud. "Yes, and it's a lot quieter and cleaner."

The two men returned to the office and discussed options for Steve's new sign.

Kent suggested a double-faced monument sign that could be read from either direction from the street. He explained the design concept and estimated cost.

"Sounds good to me," Steve said. "Let's do it."

A couple of months later, Ad-Art erected the sign on the street in front of Steve's business. That street would later be renamed Wynn Road.

Years passed before Kent received another call from Wynn. This time he wanted something slightly different than a sign.

"I've purchased property on the Strip and I'm going to build my first casino," Steve said. "I need a rendering and I want your company to do it. Here's what I have in mind."

Steve explained his concept, a tongue-in-cheek depiction of a gangster-themed casino, complete with old Packards and cartoon characters in fedora hats sporting machine guns. "I want it to look like it came right out of Chicago," he said. "Can you do it?"

Kent smiled and nodded. He'd pitched hundreds of signs for Ad-Art and had hundreds of renderings drawn up to close the deals. In the years since Betty Willis designed the "Welcome to Fabulous Las Vegas" sign, she'd moved on to work in the Ad-Art art department. Kent had hired her, not only because they were long-time friends, but because of her talent as a sign artist. He'd have Betty put Wynn's vision to paper. "First," Kent insisted, "I need to see the property."

Twenty minutes later, they were standing on the corner of Flamingo Road and Las Vegas Boulevard, looking at an empty lot adjacent to Caesars Palace. Steve stood with his hands in his pockets, looking across the 10-acre lot. "I want to call it Gangland."

"Jeez," Kent said under his breath. He looked at Steve. "Isn't calling a casino next to Caesars Palace 'Gangland' a little reckless?"

Steve shook his head, making it clear he didn't think it was an issue. "It's my land and I can put what I want on it."

The concept, as Steve envisioned it, was a comical approach to gangster life. As far as he was concerned, times were changing in Las Vegas, and the glory days of the mob were in the past.

Kent reluctantly agreed to have the rendering drawn up. Business was business and Steve had come to Kent first. Selling signs was the job and if Ad-Art didn't do the rendering, another company would. "I'll be back in touch as soon as I have something to show you."

A week later, Kent arrived at the Best Brands warehouse, rendering in hand.

"I love it." Steve looked up from the colorful illustration spread across his desk. "It's perfect, exactly what I had in mind." He rose and shook Kent's hand. "Thank you. I owe you one." He looked back down at the rendering and ran his hand across it, stopping at a section depicting two mobsters in zoot suits and fedora hats. They were emerging from a bullet-laden black sedan in front of a casino. Cigar stubs hung from their mouths as a spray of oversized bullets shot out from their machine guns onto the street in front of them. "Just perfect," he whispered.

A few days later, the floor dropped out from under Kent.

He was heading for his office at the Ad-Art warehouse when he was stopped by Dindy Clark. "Boss, a call came in from the Caesars Palace executive offices about an hour ago. It was Ruth, Mr. Jacobson's secretary." Nate Jacobson was president of Caesars Palace. "She said you were to report to the executive offices, like, now. She sounded nervous and said to tell you it was important."

"Did she say what it was about?" Kent asked, raising an eyebrow. He'd been summoned to the executive offices at Caesars on numerous occasions, but never on such short notice and with what appeared to be some urgency.

"Nope. She just said to get there as quick as you could."

Kent left the warehouse and made a beeline for Caesars Palace. He entered the elevator leading to the executive offices on the second floor. The elevator door opened to reveal Ruth Burtling, Nate Jacobson's private secretary, sitting at her desk, her eyes as big as saucers.

"They're in there," she said, pointing to a huge door leading to the corner safe room adjacent Jacobson's office. "All of them."

Ruth managed a resigned smile. She'd met many of Jacobson's business associates. He valued her as a loyal and discreet employee and, as a result, she'd been privy to sensitive information, including occasional bone-chilling rhetoric coming from open executive offices.

Today was one of those days.

"Good luck," she said with a sigh as Kent walked past her toward the door. "From the ruckus that's been going on in there all morning, I'm afraid you're going to need it."

Kent gave her a quizzical look, pushed open the door, and entered the room. He heard the five-inch-thick steel door close behind him with a thud and a heavy suction sound, followed by the clicking sound of steel pins locking into place. The bulletproof room contained no windows and housed an arsenal of weapons hidden in the back wall behind a large mahogany desk. The men gathered in the room found such precautions necessary, and with good reason.

In 1965, hotel developer Jay Sarno broke ground on construction of Caesars Palace on land leased from Kirk Kerkorian with money acquired from the International Brotherhood of Teamsters Central States Pension fund, via reputed mobster and IBT president Jimmy Hoffa. Hoffa and his business associate Allen Dorfman, consultant to the IBT, approved loans amounting to $10.6 million for the project. Sarno acquired additional funding by teaming up with Baltimore insurance executive Nate Jacobson and the two became partners in the development of Caesars Palace. Jacobson handled the money and Sarno handled concept and design.

Once the funds were secured, Sarno's friend Harry Wald was appointed project manager. Upon completion of the property in August of 1966, Wald became hotel vice-president.

Sarno, Jacobson, and Wald were important men in the Las Vegas gambling industry. They held close associations with reputed gangsters or were, as many believed, gangsters in their own right. They were all present in the room. Jacobson was standing behind the desk, surrounded by Sarno and Wald on his right and booking agent Art Engler on his left. They were all looking down at a rendering spread out in front of them on the desk.

The blood drained from Kent's face.

At the sound of the door closing, Jacobson looked up. "What the f**k were you thinking?" Jacobson screamed, sweeping Steve's rendering into his hand and nearly knocking Engler down as he stormed around the desk toward Kent.

Jacobson's eyes bulged from his beet-red face as he waved the rendering furiously in the air, inches from Kent's head. "We can't have a casino named 'Gangland' built next to Caesars Palace. Are you out of your goddamned mind?"

Kent stood frozen, at a loss for words. Ad-Art had done extensive work for Caesars Palace, including the main marquee. There was no way to explain his way out of it, but he couldn't figure out what the rendering was doing in these men's possession.

And then the bells went off. It all made sense. Wynn was a gambling man. And he wasn't the only one. Kent remembered being called into Barron Hilton's office only a few months before.

Barron Hilton was owner of both the Las Vegas Hilton and Flamingo Hilton hotel-casinos. He and a handful of executives were discussing the plausibility of purchasing the property adjacent to the Flamingo, directly across the street from the property Steve Wynn later purchased.

Barron had concerns that someone purchasing the Hughes-owned property could potentially build a structure that would block his Flamingo Hilton marquee. The conversation was between Barron Hilton and Henri Lewin, Hilton's top executive in Las Vegas. Hilton vice-president John Fitzgerald, as well as Nick Naff and Bruce Banke from public relations, were also at the meeting. Kent was included, because Ad-Art was servicing the Flamingo signage, marquee included.

"Hughes is asking a million dollars for that piece of property and that's way too much," Lewin had insisted. "Hell, it houses power lines overhead. It would be impossible to build anything of consequence on it, other than a parking lot."

Hilton wasn't sure. "Maybe it's a risk we shouldn't take."

Kent stepped in, suggesting that purchasing the property was worthwhile as insurance against any significant building in the event the power lines ever went underground. "Mr. Hilton, Ad-Art is presently doing work for the MGM and I know they're looking for additional parking for their property. They're right across the street from that lot. You might consider buying it, if only to sell or rent to the MGM."

Hilton passed on the purchase, a gamble he later came to regret when Jackie Gaughan bought the property and persuaded the power company to move the power lines. Gaughan then built the Barbary Coast, blocking the Flamingo marquee.

The impact of Wynn's rendering at Caesars Palace was no less unpleasant. Steve had no intention of building Gangland. He was banking on the idea that Caesars Palace's owners wouldn't want anything remotely resembling a gangster-themed property built next to their casino. He used the rendering as leverage to persuade Caesars Palace to purchase his property.

His gamble paid off. Caesars Palace bought the property for which Wynn paid $1 million for $2.25 million. The profit helped him achieve his real goal: another property downtown on Fremont Street.

Starting early in 1969 with the help of Las Vegas banking magnate E. Parry Thomas, Wynn began acquiring stock in the 23-year-old Golden Nugget. His quiet acquisition from interest holders eventually added up to 51%, making him majority shareholder and empowering him to take control of the casino. He completely renovated the property, including building the casino's first hotel tower in 1977, a move that forced other downtown casinos to follow suit. To this day, Steve Wynn is credited with starting the process that transformed downtown Fremont Street from a row of rundown hotel-casinos into the vibrant Fremont Street Experience it is today.

Kent survived the meeting in the safe room at Caesars Palace, but not unscathed. Sarno, Jacobson, and associates were furious over the Gangland rendering and Ad-Art's future sign contracts with Caesars decreased. Steve, on the other hand, kept his word, and when the time came to choose a sign company for his newly-acquired casino, Ad-Art was awarded a sign contract for more than a million dollars.

Gangland was never built and the Gangland rendering was never seen again.

9

A Message from Mr. Hughes

Howard Hughes was residing in the penthouse of the Desert Inn after a last-minute stay in late 1966 extended into the New Year's holiday. His flat refusal to leave his hotel suite prevented the hotel from honoring holiday guest reservations, infuriating the hotel owner Moe Dalitz, who insisted Hughes either purchase the hotel or get out.

The eccentric Mr. Hughes didn't move out. He bought the Desert Inn in the spring of 1967 for $13.25 million.

While he was living at the Desert Inn, he cast his acquiring eye on the Frontier across the street from and in view of his Strip-facing windows, but his legendary erratic behavior manifested in a somewhat strange method for starting the negotiations to buy the property.

He sent a messenger.

****

Tell Mr. Hughes He's Safe from the Sign

There was nothing particularly impressive about the young man approaching Kent in the Frontier parking lot. He was slim with sandy brown hair, in his mid-30s, and dressed in khaki pants and a long-sleeved shirt with shoulder epaulets. His gait was brisk and he carried himself like a young military recruit. He stopped directly in front of

Kent. "Do you work for the company that built this sign?" he asked.

The fact that the young man didn't bother to introduce himself wasn't particularly annoying. It was more the tone of his voice that implied an innate lack of respect. "Who's asking?"

"I work for Mr. Howard Hughes." The young man's shoulders snapped back and his chest expanded. "He has a problem with this sign." He turned on his heel and pointed to the Frontier pylon sign, towering behind him.

"Oh, he does, does he? And what that might be?" Kent said. Everyone knew who Howard Hughes was, but whatever "problem" he had with the sign, there wasn't much he could do about it. He didn't own the Frontier.

At the tone of Kent's voice, the young man faltered slightly. "Mr. Hughes owns the Desert Inn property across the street." He paused.

Kent nodded. Anyone in Las Vegas who hadn't been living under a rock knew that Hughes owned the hotel. He waited for the young man to continue.

"Mr. Hughes resides on the top floor of his property. He's concerned that this sign could fall and land on his penthouse. He wants it taken down."

Kent stifled a laugh. He imagined the look that was going to appear on John Papais's face when he told his boss about Hughes's demand. Ad-Art had charged the Frontier a small fortune to build and erect the massive sign. The young man had no clue how important a big marquee was to a casino.

But the kid was nothing more than the bearer of potential bad news and Kent's tone softened. He saw no need to make the young man's life any more difficult than it probably already was, working for a billionaire recluse like Howard Hughes. "Listen, you can tell your boss he has nothing to worry about. The total height of that sign is 189 feet and it weighs over 400 tons. From where that sign stands to Mr. Hughes's property across the street is easily three times the distance. My company built this sign and even if it were to fall, which I can assure you it will not, I hardly think it could jump that far. If he wants the sign removed, he should purchase the hotel."

The young man looked up at the sign again, then across the street to the Desert Inn. His gaze lifted to stop on the penthouse level. "I guess that makes sense," he said.

"You can go tell your boss he's perfectly safe. But make sure he understands that the sign's not coming down, not unless he wants to buy the hotel and tear it down himself."

The young man in the epaulets delivered Kent's message to Hughes: The Frontier's sign was not coming down.

Three months later, Howard Hughes bought the Frontier Hotel for $23 million. Even then, the sign wasn't taken down. And it certainly didn't fall down. Ironically, years after the purchase, Mother Nature proved that the peculiar billionaire's concerns might not have been so outrageous after all.

****

When the Wind Blows

Desert wind. It was a factor so common in Las Vegas that sign hangers accepted it as an unpleasant fact of life. Signs were designed to withstand all the elements, with wind being the biggest challenge. Structural engineers endeavored to build them to withstand the strongest gusts, but no one could accurately predict the amount of damage a windstorm could bring. Not even the strongest construction made any sign immune to the dangers of potentially cataclysmic gale forces.

Gene Sagas was employed as the Frontier hotel's senior watch engineer and was supervising his crew on swing shift when a particularly violent windstorm began to create havoc on the Strip.

The son of a Cuban father and Puerto Rican mother, Gene was born and raised in Connecticut. Upon completion of his military service, he settled in California, where he majored in biomedical engineering. He received his engineering license and was working in the hospital industry in California when a family doctor informed him that the smog in the San Fernando Valley where he and his family lived was endangering the life of his young son. The family would have to move.

Gene's California license afforded him the opportunity to accept an engineering position at Valley Hospital in Las Vegas, so in order to protect his son's health, he relocated with his family to the smog-free desert town. As it turned out, Las Vegas not only ensured his son's improved health, but it also offered Gene opportunities he never imagined. It was the '70s and Gene quickly discovered that Las Vegas was the land of opportunity for skilled individuals such as himself.

In addition to working at the hospital, he began coaching little league baseball and it wasn't long before his engineering talents caught the attention of Dennis Dietrich, an opposing team's coach, who worked as assistant chief engineer at the Frontier. He introduced Gene to Dick Whalen, the hotel's chief engineer and Gene landed a job. His position in the engineering department provided him with a good salary and great benefits in a town where the cost of living for his young family was dwarfed in comparison to what he had experienced in California. It was the beginning of what would become a long and successful career in his chosen field within the gaming industry.

The Frontier property was large and Gene's responsibilities covered not only maintenance of the building, but attention to the exterior grounds, including the marquee.

On the evening of the storm, the wind had been howling all night, with 50 mph gusts coming out of the northwest. At approximately 10 p.m., while checking the perimeter of the property, Gene encountered a frightening sight. The hotel's enormous exterior sign was coming apart. He raced back into the hotel and placed an emergency phone call.

"We've got a major problem down here," Gene began. "The windstorm's destroying the sign. The 'F' is spinning out of control."

Kent Carmichael rose from bed. "I'm on my way."

By the time Kent arrived at the Frontier, the gusts had reached over 65 mph. He pulled his truck to a stop at the base of the sign, next to another truck marked Ad-Art.

"Hey," a voice sounded out over the wind. Dennis Jaeger had arrived moments before. Dennis was one of the physically strongest men working for Ad-art, the obvious choice to call in an emergency situation like the one the two sign men were about to face.

The men exited their trucks and began unloading supplies. As they heaved reels of rope and the jugs of water they were going to need to cool them onto the ground, they looked up at the "F." Shards of metal and glass were blowing off the pylon in every direction as it spun. The men watched in horror as the speed of the spin increased. Transformers blew as sparks ignited neon gas, resulting in powerful blasts within the sign structure.

"It's caught up in a wind eddy," Dennis called, reaching into the bed of his truck for more rope. "We have to stop it."

They hurried to the base of the sign. With ropes, come-alongs and jugs in hand, they began the vertical climb up the ladder to the reader unit, twenty-five feet above. The structure shook in the wind as they continued another 40 feet up into the steel cabinet containing the spinning shaft.

"Let's do this," Kent hollered as they entered the cabinet.

The two men worked quickly, each wrapping 10-foot sections of rope in opposite directions around the 16-inch driveshaft controlling the "F." They attached come-alongs to steel stanchions on either side of the spinning shaft and hooked the ropes through the come-alongs to the steel.

"More water," Kent yelled over the howling wind and clanging of sign debris flying around them. "She's still spinning way too fast." He jerked his body to the left to avoid a chunk of sign debris flying straight toward him.

As Dennis poured water on the ropes to keep the friction from burning them, steam rose from the spinning shaft, burning their eyes.

Kent continued jacking the wrapped rope tighter around the shaft in a frantic effort to stop the spin.

"Do we have enough rope to stop it?" Dennis yelled as he jacked his rope tighter in the opposite direction. He lifted his jug and poured the remaining water over both burning ropes. "Damn. The ropes are fraying already."

Kent looked up to see the big letter still spinning. The violent vibration inside the massive structure resonated from the floor up through his legs.

A transformer popped behind them.

They fought for balance, pulling with all their strength. The muscles in their arms bulged with the strain of the pull against the ropes. Kent looked across the shaft at his friend.

Dennis was six-foot-four and 250 pounds of solid muscle. He himself was six-two and rock hard as well. After years working in the air as a sign hanger, Kent feared that if the two of them couldn't stop the spin, no one could.

"I think we're slowing it down," Dennis cried out. "Pull harder!"

As the men jacked the ropes tighter around the spinning shaft, the resistance against the force of the wind gradually began to slow the spin. The two men worked in tandem, dodging flying sign debris as broken pieces of neon flew past them. The muscles in their arms ached as they jacked the ropes tighter.

Finally, the spinning shaft came to a stop.

"That was close." Kent locked off his jacks, grabbed his jug, and poured the last of the water over the ropes. "We got lucky."

"At least we got it stopped before we lost the 'F.'" Dennis leaned against the wall, rubbing his forearms. The grimace on his face spoke volumes. Sign work wasn't for the weak.

Kent pressed his hands against his lower back and leaned forward. "Sorry, Dennis, but it's not over yet. We have to go back down and get more rope. We have to secure it properly."

The wind whistled through the damaged cabinet. Kent ducked to avoid a metal shard flying off the wall beside him. It smashed against the opposite side of the cabinet.

"Whoa, that was close," Dennis hollered, dodging another piece of debris as it flew past him and escaped out a basketball-size opening in the wall.

"Too close." Kent shook his head. "Let's get this thing secured and call it a night. We'll check the damage in the morning when we can see."

"Sounds good to me." Dennis managed a smile. He grabbed an empty jug and remnants of burnt rope that had frayed and fallen from the shaft.

The two men descended the long ladder to the ground. They retrieved more rope and come-alongs, then climbed back up into the steel structure. It was two a.m. when they finished safely securing the shaft. After they battled the wind back to their trucks, they stopped and shook hands. They didn't speak. The look they gave each other said it all. They'd just prevented a catastrophe. It was all part of the job.

Kent peered up at the damaged Frontier sign, then across the street to the penthouse of the Desert Inn. "Well, Mr. Hughes," he said to himself, "maybe you had a point after all."

The following morning, the storm had subsided.

While Gene and his dayshift maintenance crew assessed the damage to the landscaping, Ad-Art crewmembers scoured the perimeter surrounding the Frontier sign, gathering up sign debris scattered across the Frontier property and even beyond the property. Among the largest pieces of debris, a 15-pound transformer had landed in the Frontier parking lot. A second transformer was found lodged in the roof of the I-Magnin hair salon across the street. Miraculously, no one had been hit.

Once the cumulative damage had been addressed, Gene and Kent headed to the coffee shop. Both agreed that the details of the evening's calamity remain their secret.

"Considering the power of that storm last night, the sign doesn't look too badly disturbed," Gene said. "I think we got away with it this time."

"Thank goodness for that," Kent replied, "but the problem with the 'F' will have to be addressed, so this doesn't happen again in the future."

To ensure the calamity would never be repeated, John Papais insisted that a breaking disk, 22 inches in diameter, be installed on the shaft of the "F," with a governor to control the spin. Should the spin exceed a certain speed, the built-in governor would engage, stopping the spin and locking the letter into a stationary position. The cost was high, but deemed necessary to protect the integrity of a structure already expensive to maintain. The rotating letter had been designed to be a one-of–a-kind focal feature for a sign on the Strip. To the Frontier, the locked-in $3,500 monthly maintenance fee to Ad-Art was a major expense, but worth the cost. For Ad-Art, it was important to keep those maintenance costs down.

A few months after the upgrade, another windstorm hit. The governor worked perfectly, stopping the "F" in a randomly aligned position with the letter facing south.

The chance alignment gave Kent an idea. "Why not just let it rest static and see if anyone notices?"

Months passed and the "F" stood motionless. No one contacted the hotel to inquire why.

John's brother Lou, upon learning of the maintenance costs Ad-Art was saving by leaving the "F" at rest, ordered the sign crew to permanently lock it off. "Hell," he said, "no one's said anything. Let's save some money."

The Frontier sign remained in place until the sale and subsequent demolition of the hotel in 2007. Most tourists who viewed the "F" after it was permanently locked off had no idea it had ever revolved.

****

Another Message from Howard

Howard Hughes continued his casino shopping spree, purchasing the Sands and the Castaways in 1967, while still residing in the Desert Inn penthouse. Meanwhile, his paranoia over his health and personal safety grew. The next property to draw the ire of Mr. Hughes was the Silver Slipper, across the Strip and adjacent to the Frontier.

Once again, he sent an errand boy to deliver a message.

Sam Diamond sat at the desk in his executive office at the Silver Slipper. As VP and casino manager of the property, he'd come a long way since 1947, when he'd accepted a job as a floorman at mobster Bugsy Siegel's newly opened Flamingo Hotel. Sam eventually owned an interest in the resort and continued to purchase points in additional casinos, both on the Strip and downtown. It was rumored that he used his mob "ties" from the Bugsy days to do so.

It was late afternoon and Sam was an hour away from meeting Shelby Williams and a few other hotel associates for dinner. He and Shelby were close friends, a fact that had enabled him to invest a modest sum to become part-owner of the Silver Slipper, along with Shelby and his wife Claudine. The couple had purchased the casino in 1964 when it was plagued by legal troubles stemming from illegal dice games.

Sam was about to leave the office when his secretary tapped on the door and entered.

96

"Mr. Diamond, there's a young man here to see you. He has no appointment, but he says he was sent by Howard Hughes and that it's important he speak with you. Evidently, it's a matter of some urgency."

Sam raised an eyebrow. "Hughes, you say?" No one got into Sam Diamond's office without an appointment, but no one working for Howard Hughes had ever tried. "It's all right, Alice. I'll see him. Send him in."

A young man entered the office. It was the same clean-cut kid who'd spoken to Kent Carmichael about the Frontier sign. He stopped in front of Sam's desk. "Mr. Howard Hughes has a problem with your slipper."

Sam leaned back in his chair. The young man was referring to the high-heel slipper at the top of the pylon sign in front of the casino.

"And what exactly is the problem your Mr. Hughes has with it?" The stare that accompanied his question was meant to be intimidating.

It worked. The young man lowered his eyes and took a deep breath. "Well, sir, Mr. Hughes says the lights are too bright. The constant turning, and the glow shining into his penthouse windows across the street are very distracting to him. He wants you to turn them off."

Sam placed both elbows on his desk. He laced his fingers together and placed his chin squarely on his clenched hands. He mustered his most ferocious glare, raised his head slightly, and looked directly into the young man's eyes.

The young messenger was already starting to tremble.

"I don't know what your boss is smoking over there," he growled, "but there's no way in hell I'm turning off my slipper." He stood up. "You tell your boss, this is my response." He shot up the middle finger of his left hand.

"As long as I have anything to do with this place, those lights stay on. Are we clear?"

"Perfectly clear, Mr. Diamond. I'll deliver the message." The young man backed up toward the door.

"You do that," Sam said. "Now get yourself out of here. You're making me late for dinner."

The young man turned on his heel and exited the office like he was running from a fire.

Sam rose from his chair. His countenance softened and he chuckled at the thought of telling the fellows at dinner about the encounter. He knew they'd all get a big laugh out of it. "Welcome to Las Vegas, Mr. Hughes," Sam said to himself as he grabbed his hat and headed out the door. "If you want my slipper turned off, you can buy the damned place and flick the switch yourself."

Howard Hughes continued repeatedly to insist the lights be turned off. He was repeatedly refused. In April 1968, a few months after Sam Diamond's encounter with the young man in the epaulets, Hughes bought the Silver Slipper for $5.4 million.

After the Hughes purchase, the 980 twinkling lights were temporarily turned off, only to be turned back on after his departure from his suite in the Desert Inn. The slipper remained, in all its twinkling glory, until the demolition of the Silver Slipper in 1988.

In the years following the sale, Sam Diamond frequently drove along the Strip and passed the Silver Slipper. Looking up at the sparkling slipper always brought a smile to his face. Sam had invested $250,000 in the hotel in1964. When Howard Hughes bought the place three years later, his profit from the sale was in the millions.

He laughed all the way to the bank.

The slipper is preserved today in the Neon Museum in Las Vegas.

Mouse Pack Photo Memorabilia

The Silver Slipper is just one of the many iconic Las Vegas Signs torn down or imploded as the city evolved into the 21st century. Many are located in the Neon Museum, where they are seen and appreciated by thousands of visitors annually.

(Photo credit: Las Vegas News Bureau)

Binion's Gambling Hall and Hotel was formerly known as Binion's Horseshoe, and named for its founder, Benny Binion, whose family ran it from 1951 until 2004. In 1970 Benny's son, Jack began hosting the World Series of Poker (WSOP) at the Horseshoe. Eventually, the WSOP became the largest set of poker tournaments in the world. (Photo credits: Las Vegas News Bureau)

Cranes lift Frontier Sign into position as sign hangers look on.

(Frontier sign photo from Kent's personal collection)

A river of cars is piled up against the barrier between the Strip and Caesars Palace parking lot after the massive flood over July 4th weekend, 1975.

The MGM fire of 1980 killed 85 people and injured 700 more.

Five hundred firefighters responded to the blaze.

Curt made a bet with his slot machine department at Boomtown in 1993. "If You gentlemen can up your profits this month, I'll dress up for one full day in a cocktail waitress uniform. If you lose, every last one of you has to do the same." Curt lost.

Curt in Congo Room at the Sahara with Muhammed Ali

Curt with Jake LaMotta and Rocky Graciano

(right) Gene and Kent at Boomtown

(center below) Mr. O'Lucky smiles down on Fremont Street

(below) Country Superstars packed the Fitz during NFR.

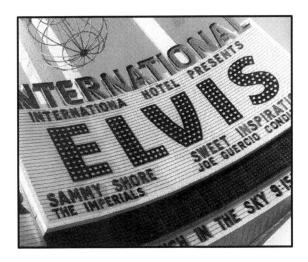

Kirk Kerkorian opened the International Hotel in 1969, the first true mega-resort and the first to utilize architect Martin Stern Jr.'s distinctive tri-form, with room wings radiating from the central service core. Elvis broke attendance records performing in the International Theater.

The International was sold to Barron Hilton in 1970 and renamed the Las Vegas Hilton in 1971. Elvis continued to perform to sold-out crowds until 1976. (Photo credit: Las Vegas News Bureau)

THE
FRONTIER
and
Beyond Belief

Gildah the elephant

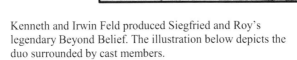

Kenneth and Irwin Feld produced Siegfried and Roy's legendary Beyond Belief. The illustration below depicts the duo surrounded by cast members.

THE MINT 400

Thousands gathered on Fremont Street to watch the beginning of the race. (Photo credit: Las Vegas News Bureau)

Norm, with his brother, gets ready to race. (below) Norm and Parnelli Jones drive buggy in Mint 400.

Kent and Debbie Reynolds pose backstage at the Hilton prior to Debbie's Hollywood Memorabilia Fashion Show.

Debbie and Todd Fisher at the sound board at Debbie's Star Theater.

Debbie's head shot. She carried them with her always and signed photos for thousands of fans. (Photos courtesy of Todd Fisher and the Reynolds Collection.)

When Joe Rosenthal, Hilton Corporation planning VP, saw the model of the proposed Flamingo Hilton marquee created by Heath and Co., he told Barron Hilton, "You have to see this." The model was placed in front of a black backdrop and top lit with tiny pin spots in the Flamingo's conference room. Hilton was overwhelmed by the stunning model and Heath landed the contract.

Barron Hilton signs $1.5 million contract. Witnessing the signing are, left to right, Henri Lewin, senior vice president of Hilton Hotels' western division; Kent Carmichael, production manager for Heath and Co.; Milt Lloyd, president of Heath; Joe Rosenthal, vice president of Hilton Corporation planning and construction, and Raul Rodriguez, designer of the lighting and sign system. (Photo credit: *Las Vegas Review-Journal*)

Who Will Stand?

Jerry stands in front of an American flag containing the names of all the individuals killed in the 9.11. Terrorist attacks. Printed beneath the flag, a tribute to those fallen souls includes these words: "Now and forever it will represent their immortality. We shall never forget them."

(left to right) *Who Will Stand?* Director of Photography, Michael Bedik, Director Phil Valentine, Mayor Oscar Goodman, and executive producer, Jerry Gillock. Honored at the Sundance Film festival, *Who Will Stand?* appears regularly on the Documentary Channel and was featured at the 2016 Democratic Convention where its theme song was sung by Clint Holmes.

Soldiers in Iraq place flag on front of Humvee.

(Photo credit: Las Vegas News Bureau)

The iconic Silver Slipper and Frontier marquees stood adjacent to each other on the Las Vegas Strip.

On the right, the Slipper as it appears today, on display at the Neon Museum. (Photo from Gene's personal collection)

Sam Diamond refused demands by Howard Hughes to turn off the lights of the Slipper.

(Sam Diamond's photo courtesy of Sam's son, Freddy Diamond)

THE STARDUST

Cranes lift Stardust sign pieces 200 feet into the air.

The Stardust sign on display at the Neon Museum (Photos from Kent's personal collection)

"Vision Over Vegas," taken at the Top of the Mint Hotel, graced
media networks worldwide, celebrating a magical era in Las Vegas.
(Photo courtesy of Lorraine Perry Hunt Bono)

Elvis impersonator Johnny Harra and comedian Redd Foxx headlined
at Major Riddle's Silverbird Hotel.

Country Takes Over Las Vegas!

Country music rocks Fremont Street as visitors flock to see free shows. Country superstar Toby Keith was one of many who entertained crowds downtown.

Meanwhile, the 600-seat Opera Dinner Theater in the Boomtown Casino offered "Direct from Opryland…Nashville U.S.A.," a high-powered tribute to the best of country music.

Welcome
to
Fabulous
Las Vegas!

Original sign 1959
(Photo credit: Las Vegas News Bureau)

Sign as it stands today.

10

I Knew Him When

As Las Vegas entered the 1970s, downtown casinos continued to struggle against the competition stretching down Las Vegas Boulevard. Lavish hotel-casinos on the Strip continued to offer high-stakes gambling, as well as the irresistible draw of high-profile entertainment. The Rat Pack literally packed the Sands with high-rollers and, across the street, Caesars Palace booked Andy Williams and the Lennon Sisters, huge stars during that era. Liberace performed to sold-out crowds at the Riviera and when Elvis Presley appeared on the scene at the International in 1969, the Strip and vicinity reigned, like "The King" himself, as the only place to be.

As the stakes grew higher for downtown casino owners, the only choice was to take heed of what was happening on the Strip and follow suit. Golden Nugget executives wooed entertainers with lavish contracts loaded with perks and held special events to draw the public into the casino.

When an unusual news article out of San Francisco caught the eye of Norm Johnson, who'd moved on from the Mint and was now working as director of public relations at the Nugget, he saw opportunity knocking.

It was Wednesday September 11, 1974, and Norm sat, shaking his head in amused disbelief, as he read the news article: A group of senior citizens living in an elderly care facility in San Francisco had been arrested and jailed for holding an "illegal" penny-ante poker game in the rec-room at their senior center.

"I'll be a son of a bitch," Norm said. He headed for Steve Wynn's office (he, along with a group of investors, had taken over control of the historic Nugget casino in 1973, after Wynn's successful purchase of the property.) As head of public relations, it was Norm's job to publicize and promote the hotel and he had an idea that would do just that. All he had to do was convince the boss.

"Steve, we have one hell of an opportunity here," Norm began, handing him a copy of the story. "We should fly these old codgers down here, feed them, house them over at the Four Queens, give them their own poker table, and let the world know what you did for them. We can set up a special poker table in the poker room, give 'em some chips to play, and publicize the hell out of it."

Steve's eyebrows lifted. It was an unorthodox idea. "Go on. How many are we talking about?"

"The story said nine were arrested," Norm replied. "I have no idea if they can all make it, but I've talked to one of the caretakers and he said most of them were okay to travel."

Steve leaned back in his chair. "I like it. Let's do it. "How soon do you think we can get this thing going?"

Norm went back to his office and asked his secretary Kelly to call Herb Kelleher, co-founder of Southwest Airlines. He'd met with Herb a couple of times and knew Southwest could use the publicity. He also knew the media would be all over it, especially the TV networks.

Pretty soon Kelly had located Kelleher and Norm was on the phone. "We'll fly out of McCarran and I think I'll need fifteen or sixteen same-day round-trip tickets, depending on how many of the local television stations want to make the trip. Two days later, you can return the passengers to San Francisco."

James Dean, hotel entertainment director who shared office space with Norm, entered the office just as Johnson was ending the call with Herb. "What crazy idea you got going this time?" he asked as he slid behind his desk.

After explaining the idea and letting him know that Wynn had approved it, James agreed with Norm that the Golden Nugget would make the old codgers famous and the press would eat it up. "A human-interest story like this could put our poker room on the map."

As predicted, Southwest Airlines jumped at the idea. And Norm convinced two of the television channels, NBC's TV 3 and CBS's TV 8, to make the trip. Channel 13 would pick up the story when the plane landed on Monday. The Las Vegas Review-Journal and Las Vegas Sun daily newspapers both assigned reporters to cover the festivities. The plans were finalized when six of the nine San Francisco seniors agreed to fly to Vegas.

And the fireworks began.

Once the plane with the Las Vegas media landed in San Francisco, two stretch limos made their way to the senior-living facility, where the group of nine recently released "convicts" waited. A group of local television stations and reporters were there to report on the event. As the six elderly San Franciscans hugged the three unable to make the trip, flashbulbs were popping. With bags in hand, they climbed into the limos. The media from Las Vegas documented the flight back to Las Vegas, photographing, taping, and interviewing the poker players, and by the time the plane landed in Las Vegas, the publicity machine was revving like an eight-cylinder race car. Every local television station in Las Vegas covered the group's arrival. The Golden Nugget arranged to accommodate the San Francisco group in rooms at the adjacent Four Queens, comped them meals and booze at the Nugget, and supplied each with poker chips.

Mayor Oran Gragson, Sheriff Ralph Lamb, and Steve Wynn greeted the band of six illegal gamblers as the limos pulled up to the casino. A special table in the poker room was set up for the San Francisco "kids" and with the blessing of the Las Vegas Police Department, play began.

A special guest invited by Steve, Amarillo Slim (the 1972 World Series of Poker Champion) arrived and asked if he could sit in for a couple of hands.

Viva Vaughn, 82, the youngest of the group, stood up and hugged Slim. The fun was off and running. They played poker for two days, leaving Las Vegas on Wednesday Sept. 18, with a brand-new $100 bill in their wallet or purse, courtesy of Steve Wynn.

News of the event went national. Every network from Los Angeles to New York covered the unlikely group of gamblers as they enjoyed the hospitality of the Golden Nugget, gambling legally in Sin City.

Norm was right. The investment was worth its weight in gold. The positive publicity generated by the brilliant advertising gimmick raised the reputation of the Golden Nugget poker room above all others downtown and put it on the map in a big way. Attendance doubled and sparked the rise of what is even today one of the city's most popular poker-playing venues. Golden Nugget poker tournaments draw players by the hundreds, delivering huge payouts to the best poker players in the world. It also raised the profile of the World Series of Poker, which is now among the top 10 richest sporting events in the world.

****

Elvis Is in the Building!

As the Nugget prospered, smaller downtown casinos searched for fresh new faces to ignite interest in their prospective properties. If they couldn't land a star, they'd find the next best thing.

So entered the birth of the impersonator.

In 1969, the Mint Hotel added a lounge to the property. It seated 120 people. In the years that followed, Curt Thompson, as hotel manager, was in charge of booking the entertainment for the lounge. The list of entertainers he hired included Sam Butera and Freddie Bell, as well as other popular local Las Vegas draws. One day in 1977 Curt was called into the office of Andrew Zorne, the hotel's VP and general manager.

"Curt," Andrew began, "we have to get more gamblers into this casino. I want you to find an act that will pack our new lounge, something that will get tourists on the Strip to take notice."

Curt returned to his office and started making calls. After speaking with a few agents, one of them made an unusual offer.

"I've got a guy in Texas named Johnny Harra. He's willing to fly in to Vegas with his band and his back-up singers and audition for you. He'll do it for free. Trust me. He's perfect for your lounge. You'll love him."

Curt was skeptical. He couldn't imagine why any decent band would be willing to travel for no money and no guarantee of a contract. The agent didn't give many details and the offer sounded too good to be true.

Curt said so. "Look, send me his promo packet and a cassette. If I like him, I'll call you back."

A day later, the packet arrived. When Curt opened it and pulled out the promo photos, he couldn't believe his eyes. "Good God," he said to himself. Johnny Harra's resemblance to Elvis Presley was uncanny. But booking an impersonator was a risky move. The real Elvis was an enormous star. He packed the Hilton showroom when he played Las Vegas. Thanks to Curt's friend and former roommate Dan Celeste, who held the position of food and beverage controller at the Hilton, Curt had seen Elvis perform live several times.

Curt sat with his eyes glued to Harra's headshot. If he could sing like Elvis, it would be quite a novelty. And a great draw for the lounge. It might be worth the gamble.

Curt took another look at the headshot. He reached for the cassette included in the promo package and popped it into his tape player. He held the man's photo in one hand and pushed the play button with the other. "Please be good," he prayed.

The music started and the man on the tape began to sing. Curt felt his heartbeat quicken as he listened to the singer's voice. Halfway through the second song, he pushed the stop button. He leaned back in his chair and took a deep breath. "Oh my God."

He picked up the phone and dialed the number printed on the bottom of the singer's head shot. Curt introduced himself. "I just heard your demo. We're flying you up here. You and your band. You've got an audition for a one-week gig. Then, we'll see."

On the afternoon of Johnny Harra's evening audition, he and his band began a private rehearsal in the Mint lounge. Closed drapes separated the lounge from the casino floor, but the music filtered out through the fabric into the casino. Within minutes, a huge crowd began to form outside the lounge.

"That sounds like Elvis," a giddy female tourist cried out to her companion. "I'd know that voice anywhere," she said, rushing toward the music coming from the lounge. "Nobody sounds like Elvis. It's him."

A security guard standing at the lounge entrance stopped her before she could pass through the drapes, but the crowd continued to grow. Soon, more than 150 people stood crammed up against one another, clamoring for a peek at who was playing inside the lounge.

Security called Curt's office. "You might want to get down here, boss. We've got a near riot in the casino," the guard said. "There's a mob in front of the lounge. They're convinced Elvis Presley's inside. I keep telling them it's not Elvis, but they don't believe me."

"Call extra security if you need it," Curt said with a smile. The gamble was going to pay off. He hung up the phone and called Andrew Zorne. "Andy, we've got a mob of tourists downstairs going nuts over the music coming from inside the lounge. I'm opening up Johnny Harra's audition tonight to the public and I think you're going to want to be there. We've hit the jackpot."

Rumors about an Elvis sighting at the Mint spread throughout the afternoon and Johnny Harra's "audition" became a full-blown evening's performance when the audience refused to let Johnny and his band leave the stage. They demanded encore after encore.

"You've really done it, Curt," Andrew hollered over the screams of hysterical females filling the lounge and pressing up against the stage as the two stood in the back witnessing the scene.

"Yeah, we got lucky with this guy. Listen to those women. They love him," he added, unable to hide his satisfaction. Curt Thompson had discovered the first Elvis impersonator to perform in Las Vegas.

"Sign him quick," Andrew said.

That night, Curt offered Johnny and his group an open-ended contract. Word spread like wildfire. Johnny Harra, the ultimate Elvis impersonator, began breaking every attendance record in the book. He beat out all other entertainers in the downtown casino lounges and doubled the number of gamblers in the casino.

But Curt's luck was about to run out. Word of Johnny's talent and popularity spread to the Strip and caught the attention of Major Riddle, owner of the Silverbird Hotel-Casino. A few months into Johnny's run, Curt was alerted that Major would be attending one of Johnny's shows. The news was worrisome. There was only one reason why Major would venture downtown. He'd heard about Johnny Harra. And he was interested.

Major Riddle arrived at the hotel, accompanied by none other than Norm Johnson, formerly of the Mint and Golden Nugget and now the Silverbird's marketing guru. Norm had been scouting for entertainment for the Silverbird and had taken his wife to see Harra perform the week before. With the recent death of Elvis capturing the headlines, Norm saw an opportunity to steal the next best thing.

Curt insisted on joining them for the show.

As the three men sat waiting for the show to begin, Norm reminisced about his first days living in Las Vegas.

"Did I ever tell you about my spa day with the Rat Pack at the Sands?" he said, swirling the glass of scotch he held in his hand and smiling like a Cheshire cat.

Curt rolled his eyes. He'd heard the story a hundred times. Major, however, had never heard it.

Norm leaned back in his chair and flashed back to an afternoon in 1965…

****

Norm Has a Spa Day with the Rat Pack

He was sitting at his desk at the *Las Vegas Sun* when the phone rang.

It was the paper's operator. "It's Al Silvani on the phone, Norm."

"Patch him through, hon," Norm said, aware that Silvani would be calling for one reason only. Frank Sinatra either wanted to talk to or see him.

Silvani was formerly both a good boxer and trainer. Norm had met him when he was working for Joe Louis in Los Angeles promoting fights and Joe was President of United World Enterprises. Sinatra and his buddies attended many of the fights staged at the Moulin Rouge Nightclub in Hollywood and Al and Sinatra became good friends. Silvani, as a former boxer, had the physique of a bodyguard and was always with Sinatra.

When Norm moved to Las Vegas as a featured sports columnist for the *Sun* in 1965, he and Al remained in contact. Al stayed in shape after his boxing career ended, and years later, he went on to star as a cut-man in the famous series of *Rocky* movies, starting in 1976.

"Hey, Al. What can I do for you?" Norm answered.

"The guys are taking over the spa at the Sands tomorrow afternoon at three p.m. and Frank told me to call and let you know you're invited."

Sinatra, Dean Martin, Sammy Davis, Jr., and the other members of the famous Rat Pack were performing at the Sands and though it was during working hours, the invitation to join them was too good to pass up.

"Wouldn't miss it," Norm replied, grinning. "I'll see you tomorrow."

At 3 p.m. sharp the following day, Norm walked up to a beautiful white building, located between the Sands casino and the hotel, situated a few yards from the property's fantastic blue swimming pool. He approached a Sands security officer who was checking IDs and introduced himself. "I'm an invited guest of Mr. Sinatra."

The security officer checked the guest list and allowed him to pass.

As Norm entered the spa, the sensation of being invited to a special event by the Chairman of the Board himself really began to sink in. He felt like royalty.

When Norm entered the spa, he was greeted by the wait-staff and given a key to a locker, where he undressed, wrapped himself in a beautiful thick white robe, and proceeded to the steam room.

When he entered the steam room, he stopped and took a deep breath.

"Wow," he whispered to himself. In front of him sat Sinatra, Martin, Sammy, and Silvani.

Al pointed to a seat on the bleacher and Norm sat down—with three of the greatest entertainers in the world. It was well-known fact when the Rat Pack took over the Sands spa, no one else was allowed in unless they were invited. The whole building was theirs.

For the next two hours, the group joked around, played water polo in the heated pool, and generally had a ton of fun.

When Norm returned home, he told his wife all about his afternoon. "I still can't believe it and I doubt anybody else will either. Me, hanging out with the Rat Pack, in a steam room."

The experience didn't end there. That night, accompanied by his wife, Norm attended the early show at the Sands and visited the entertainers backstage in the green room following the show.

The green room was packed with entertainers from shows up and down the Strip who had come to visit the

Pack. After-show parties were all a part of the magic of Las Vegas in those days and this night was no different from countless others.

Norm was sitting beside his wife, enjoying the festivities, when he was approached by Sammy Davis Jr.

"Say, man, I've invited a group of gypsies (dancers) and musicians up to my suite tonight after the second show. I'm doing some cooking. You and your wife are welcome to join us. The more the merrier."

Sammy's after-show parties in his suite were the stuff of legends. They frequently went on until the sun was rising the following day.

"Thanks, Sammy, but it's been a long day. How about a rain check?"

"Any time, man. Today was a groove," he said with a wink. "We have to do it again soon."

It had been a special day and evening for Norm and, to this day, one he's never forgotten. He later heard about the party he and his wife had missed that night.

Sammy loved to cook when he was on the road entertaining. He had two huge Louis Vuitton suitcases filled with pots, pans, seasonings, oils, and other essentials to cook a feast for his friends. Wherever he went, so did those suitcases.

And the man could prepare food, everything from steaks to his own famous homemade chili.

That night, Norm later heard, Sammy's suite was packed with showkids playing music and dancing, while Sammy, Camel cigarette hanging from his lips, stood over his burner cooking steaks for everyone. He ran a Bogart movie for the group, retrieved from an enormous suitcase of VHS tapes that also accompanied him on the road. The party had lasted into the wee hours of the morning.

Insiders know that in the '80s, Sammy got hooked on a new game. He insisted on having a Ms. Pac-Man machine placed in his suite when he was in Las Vegas. He spent hours on the machine and, although he accepted challenges from all comers, he almost always won. He watched in amusement as showkids screamed in delight, frantically competing against each other to try to beat their host, superstar Sammy, the champion of the Ms. Pac-Man machine.

****

Sinatra's Legendary Largesse

Back in 1963, Sinatra had gotten in trouble after Sam Giancana, a Chicago Mafia leader, was seen at the Cal-Neva, a north Lake Tahoe casino partly owned by Frank. Nevada was going through the process of revoking his gaming license when, in order to help Sinatra, Norm was asked by a friend to write a favorable story about him.

The task was easy, as Norm knew one personally.

He had recently called Sinatra to tell him about a waitress working at a place where Frank sometimes stopped to eat. "Frank, she's in the hospital and needs some help."

Sinatra had a friend take a blank signed check to the hospital with instructions to fill out the amount she was billed when she left the hospital, which turned out to be nearly $15,000. Plus, Norm heard rumors that the waitress also received an envelope stuffed with $100 bills.

Unfortunately, Norm's article didn't do Sinatra any good with the Gaming Control Board. They made him an example of how they ruled over the Nevada casino business and jerked his license, forcing him to sell his points in the Cal Neva Lodge.

126

But it didn't change Frank's predisposition for charity. He was widely known throughout the Las Vegas entertainment community as a man who often heard about some entertainer who, down on his luck, needed a helping hand, and he reached out personally to help. Sinatra was not only a great well-known entertainer, he was a great silent humanitarian.

For all those fortunate enough to experience the show business era of the Rat Pack, it was magic. As Sammy used to say, "That was Vegas, baby."

Riddle Ransoms Harra Anyway

"That's one hell of a story, Norm," Major Riddle said as the lights dimmed and the curtain began to rise on Johnny Harra's show.

"Quite an act you've got yourself, Curt," Major commented as the men watched the show together.

"As close to Elvis as you can get," Curt replied. "Now, you wouldn't be planning on stealing him away from us, would you, Major?"

Major offered a sly smile at Norm and Curt saw the writing on the wall. Only months into Johnny's contract, Major Riddle offered him his own show on the Las Vegas Strip at the Silverbird.

Johnny walked into Curt's office to give him the news. "They've offered me a contract to perform on the Strip, right down the street from where Elvis played. I'm really sorry, Curt. It's a lot of money and it's an offer I just can't refuse."

Curt put on a brave face to hide his disappointment over losing the budding star he'd discovered. "You're going to miss us here at the Mint, Johnny, but we all wish you well," Curt said on Johnny's closing night.

A few months later, Curt's phone rang. Johnny was calling from the Silverbird. "Curt, you have to help me. I'm lonely out here on the Strip. You have to find me a girl."

"What?" Curt exclaimed. "There must be a million girls dying to go out with you."

"Please, Curt. I'm talking about a 'special girl.' You know what I mean?"

Curt knew exactly what he meant. So did every bell captain working in Las Vegas. Curt made a call and Johnny got a girl.

When Johnny opened the door of his suite, he nearly fainted at the sight of the beautiful young woman standing in front of him.

"Hi," she said. "Can I come in?"

Johnny took a deep breath. She was a dead ringer for Elvis's bride, Priscilla. He was in love before she even told him her name.

Johnny wined and dined his new love, showering her with lavish gifts, Elvis-style, and it wasn't long before she felt the same way about him. Unfortunately, her "manager" did not. When Johnny convinced her to leave the escort business, he angered her pimp and things got dicey. In the words of many Vegas old-timers, "This was Vegas in the early days."

Rumor had it that due to a confrontation with the man, Johnny disappeared, taking his lady friend and leaving Las Vegas to secretly hide out somewhere in Boulder City.

Major Riddle tells it another way.

A year into Johnny's run, the anniversary of Elvis' birthday was approaching and Johnny wanted to do something special to honor his hero. He sat in Major's office and made his pitch. "Major," Johnny began, in his best Elvis drawl, "I want to do an Elvis anniversary tribute show that's free, for everybody."

"What the hell are you talking about, free?"

"I think it should be a free show, so we don't make any money off his anniversary."

Major didn't skip a beat. "No. No. No. This is Vegas. My God, this is one night we can actually make some *real* money. If we're going to do this, we're charging."

The special show to honor Elvis was scheduled and a younger Elvis impersonator was booked to perform the first half the show, an opening act of sorts, a move that upset Harra.

On the evening of the tribute show, the showroom was sold out. The younger Elvis impersonator opened to an enthusiastic crowd, then relinquished the stage to Harra. Midway through his show, Johnny stopped the music. In his best Elvis accent, Johnny addressed the audience. "Ladies and gentlemen, I'm going to pay for your tickets tonight. You just go to the cage, turn in your tickets, and they'll refund your money."

Major Riddle sat in his King's Row booth, seething. That was the night Johnny got fired.

Johnny eventually resurfaced back in Texas, minus the Priscilla look-alike, and his career lasted decades.

To this day, many consider him to be the best Elvis impersonator of all time.

****

Johnny Be Good

Johnny Harra became a big star in his own right, but it was Curt Thompson at Del Webb's Mint Hotel who gave him his first big break. For that, Curt felt a sense of pride. He knew Johnny Harra as more than a great entertainer. At all times, he was a polite and genuinely kind man. He never left character, speaking like Elvis, dressing like Elvis, and sharing Elvis's love of fine food and women. Curt just smiled when Johnny ordered room-service tables filled with pie and cake and cases of liquor to be delivered to his suite in the Mint.

He didn't change his ways during his engagement at the Silverbird. In fact, as his waistline expanded, Major Riddle called him to his office. "Johnny, I'll give you a thousand dollars a week extra for every pound you lose."

Offer or not, Johnny's waistline kept expanding and he never collected a dime of that extra money.

He was living Elvis's life to the fullest. He was packing in the crowds and thrilling them with his performances.

As far as Johnny was concerned, he was Elvis.

11

The Colonel and the Teddy Bears

In the years before Johnny Harra performed at the Mint and Silverbird, Curt's old roommate Dan Celeste was catering to the real Elvis.

Dan had climbed the ranks and held an executive position as food and beverage controller at the International on Paradise Road, a long block off the Las Vegas Strip. The hotel was owned by Kirk Kerkorian, another of the corporate moguls contributing to the ongoing takeover of the mob-controlled hotels.

In a corporate world, casino executives frequently wore several hats and this was the case with Dan Celeste. In addition to his normal routine, he was frequently asked by Chris Karamanos, general manager of operations, to monitor convention-center special events and cater to the needs of high rollers, entertainers, and other VIPs staying in the hotel. He also worked with other casino executives to solve problems unrelated to his position when they arose, including running the occasional random errand.

"Get me that check." Karamanos gave Dan the task of collecting back rent from a tenant in the International's retail area. "Barda's two months overdue and owes us three thousand. Don't come back without it."

Dan approached a young woman working behind a counter at Barda of Milan jewelry store and asked to see Gabriel Barda, the owner. It was his first time meeting the man and Dan had made it clear to Chris that he wished it could have been under more pleasant circumstances. Collecting money like a mob enforcer wasn't his job. He was food and beverage. But Chris had been firm. The rent was past due, period.

The woman offered a polite reply. "Mr. Barda's not here, but I'll get our manager." She retreated to a back room and a few minutes later, Mordechai Yerushalmi appeared. He offered his hand and a broad smile. "I'm Mordechai. I manage the store. What can I do for you?"

Dan introduced himself. "Chris Karamanos sent me down to collect the rent."

Mordechai waved a hand in the air and replied, his voice nonchalant, "Oh, I just talked to Chris. I'll have it tomorrow."

"I'm sorry, but Chris was clear that I wasn't to leave without the check," Dan insisted. He raised his eyebrows and gave Mordechai his best authoritative look.

"No, no. I promise," Mordechai responded. "I've spoken with Mr. Barda and I just got off the phone with Chris. It's OK, really. Come back tomorrow and I'll have the check for you."

Dan shrugged. "Well, this is a little unusual. I don't know you and you don't know me, but I'll trust you." He hoped Chris would feel the same way.

Dan returned to Chris's office. "He said he'd have it tomorrow."

"Yeah, yeah, he just called me. Go back tomorrow."

The following day, Dan returned to retrieve the check. He was standing in the shop, waiting for Mordechai, when a beautiful ring in the display case caught his eye. His birthday was coming up in a few months, but $1,200 was a lot of money.

He was agonizing over the ring when Mordechai appeared, check in hand.

"Mr. Celeste. As I promised, here's the check." He handed it to Dan. "You seem interested in one of our rings. Which one do you like?"

Dan pointed to a platinum ring with an oval diamond in the center, framed by two diamond baguettes.

"She's a beauty," Mordechai said, pulling his shoulders back and flashing a smile that oozed of pride over the treasures on display in his shop.

"Yes, but a bit over my budget," Dan replied. Jewelry at Barda of Milan was pricey, even for hotel executives.

"I'll make you a deal on it," he countered.

"Well, thanks, but I'm not exactly ready. I'll think about it. I've got to get going. Thanks for the check."

A few weeks passed and Dan was back in Barda, leaning over the jewelry counter. Mordechai saw him once again admiring the platinum ring. "Dan, I know you like that ring. I'll sell it to you for six hundred dollars."

"That's a great discount," Dan said with a sigh. Even at half-price, it was over his budget. He was a young executive, just getting started in life. He couldn't afford it. "I appreciate the offer, but it's still a little too rich for my blood."

Mordechai nodded. "Well, the offer stands, when you're ready."

Dan took one last look at the ring and left the store.

Early in the morning a few days after his second visit to the jewelry store, Dan woke to the sound of his beeper going off. He looked at the clock on his bedside table. "Great, a call from the hotel at six-thirty in the morning," he grumbled, reaching across his bed for the phone. He wiped the sleep from his eyes and called the hotel.

The operator answered. "Hi, Dan. Please hold for Colonel Parker."

Dan groaned. Colonel Tom Parker was Elvis Presley's manager. He was a brilliant marketer and strategist and the mastermind behind transforming Elvis from a rebellious teenager into a mainstream superstar. He controlled every facet of his client's life. And he didn't take no for an answer. Ever.

Dan yawned. "I wonder what the Colonel wants this time."

The Colonel's loud voice boomed from the other end of the line, "Dan, good. I don't want to order through room service. Those guys are in a fog. They always screw it up. You call them and order for me. Include what you want, and show up at eight o'clock. We have business to discuss." He told Dan what he wanted for breakfast and hung up.

Dan made a call to room service at the hotel and placed the Colonel's order. He made it to Colonel Parker's office by 8 a.m. The Colonel's accommodations included a set of suites on the fourth floor. An end-suite extended to the next room that acted as his office. Across the hall, other suites accommodated members of his working entourage and visiting guests of the Colonel's.

"Let's talk business," Colonel Parker said.

Dan sat drinking his coffee and watching the Colonel eat breakfast. "Business" was always about Elvis.

"I'm coordinating the arrival of Elvis's next show," Colonel Parker said, "and that includes a new promotion with teddy bears and Elvis scarves."

Dan nodded. "I Just Want to Be Your Teddy Bear" was one of Elvis's biggest hits and he threw teddy bears into the audience during the number to be grabbed by lucky audience members. When he broke into strains of "I Can't Help Falling in Love with You," the sweaty scarves Elvis removed from his neck to wrap around those of female audience members sent the women in attendance into fits of hysteria.

"I just talked to Elvis in Memphis. He won't be in town for a couple of months, but we need to get on this teddy-bear thing right away. We'll be bringing in a couple of thousand teddy bears and a slew of Elvis scarves. Not only will he toss them out during his shows but we'll also sell them to the public at a booth in the lobby."

Dan listened as the Colonel continued. "Elvis has a favorite charity here, Ruby Thomas School Program for the Deaf."

Dan was familiar with the school. It was an integral part of the Clark County School District's program for special-needs children. "So," he asked, "the proceeds from the sale of the teddy bears and scarves will go to the Ruby Thomas School to benefit the students?"

"Exactly," the Colonel said. "I need you to coordinate the whole deal when these bears come in—delivery, unpacking, inventory, pricing, setting up the booth. Volunteers from the school staff will sell the bears and scarves. You know the drill."

"Of course, Colonel. Whatever you need."

"I know this is going to be a lot of work for you, so for every teddy bear sold, you're going to get a nickel." The Colonel leaned back in his chair and crossed his arms. "Fair is fair, Dan."

Dan balked at the idea, which screamed unethical. "That's a kind thought, but I don't think I can do that. I'd have to run that by the executive offices."

The Colonel raised his hands in mock concern. "It's not much of a kickback. I doubt it'll alert the IRS." He winked. "Not at a nickel a bear. Don't worry about it. I'll take care of it."

Dan did worry about it, but there was nothing to be gained by crossing the Colonel. Just to be safe, he checked with Chris Karamanos in the executive offices.

Chris blew it off. "Look, if you get a bonus, you get a bonus. Just do it and forget about it. Take care of the Colonel."

Every day during Elvis's engagement, Dan met with the Colonel to keep him apprised of how the booth sales were going, but the early-morning room service calls still came in. Very early on the morning of August 20, well into Elvis's summer run, Dan's beeper went off. He yawned, stretched, and called the hotel. It was the Colonel again.

Ordinary people imagined that being an executive at the International must be a glamorous job. Dan, like any executive working at the hotel, knew the idea was laughable. His birthday was starting out like any other day—early. He took a shower, got dressed, and headed for the hotel.

Dan and the Colonel were drinking coffee and discussing details of Elvis's upcoming return to the International when Dan's beeper went off again.

"Sorry," Dan said. "But I should get this."

The interruption annoyed the Colonel and it showed on his face. He pointed to the phone on his desk. "Use this one."

Dan called the switchboard. The hotel operator connected him to a caller on hold. After a few minutes, Dan ended the call and apologized to the Colonel. "I'm so sorry, but it was my dad calling to wish me a happy birthday."

The Colonel's demeanor changed instantly. "Today's your birthday?" he asked, his voice booming. "Why didn't you tell me?"

Dan hid his amusement. The Colonel was actually upset he didn't know it was Dan's birthday. The Colonel was the kind of man who fancied himself in the know on all things. And for a man who was all business, he did have a heart.

"Well, happy birthday, Dan."

"Thanks, sir," Dan replied.

He had no idea that the morning's exchange would soon come into play in a surprising way.

Sales of the Elvis teddy bears were even stronger than expected; they sold out within a few days and were re-ordered several times during Elvis's performance dates. The day Elvis's month-long gig at the International ended, Ruby Thomas Elementary School received a check for $25,000. The size of the donation surpassed the amount actually collected for the sale of the items by thousands of dollars and everyone knew why. Elvis was as famous for his generosity as for his talent. He'd added his own personal contribution to the fund.

The following day, as Elvis and his entourage were preparing to leave the hotel, Dan was once again summoned up to Colonel Parker's office.

"Come on in, Dan." The Colonel greeted him with a warm handshake. "Remember how I told you you'd get a nickel for every teddy bear?"

Before Dan had a chance to answer, the Colonel continued. "You did a fine job. Here's a check." He picked up a check resting on his desk, made out to Dan from All Star Shows, the company owned and operated for Elvis by the Colonel, and handed it to him.

The gesture caught Dan off guard. He had qualms about accepting what could be considered an illegal kickback.

The Colonel looked at Dan's face. "Relax, Dan. It's a gift. Now, go buy that ring."

The Colonel was all about business, but he treated people loyal to him very well. The man would never consider giving anyone something for nothing, but when a job was well done, it was rewarded. Business was business and Dan had delivered the goods. And as was his way, the Colonel had figured out how to show his gratitude.

Although Dan was never ever able to figure out exactly how the Colonel found out about the ring, he did know there was no such thing as a coincidence when it came to the Colonel.

The check was in the amount of $600.

Dan made his way to Barda of Milan. Sales tax was 6%. So thanks to Elvis, the Colonel, and pallets of teddy bears, Dan got his ring for $36 out of pocket.

12

You Want It Where?

Kirk Kerkorian sold the International to Barron Hilton in 1970 and it was renamed the Las Vegas Hilton in 1971 (it's now Westgate Las Vegas). Dan Celeste stayed onboard as food and beverage controller while the hotel made the transition.

Elvis continued to perform in the showroom. The Colonel continued to make daily demands of hotel management throughout Elvis's engagements. Whatever Elvis wanted, he got, and the Colonel's concerns were now crossing the desk of Henri Lewin, the new hotel president under Barron Hilton. But whenever possible, men in the upper chain of command under Henri attempted to field the Colonel's ongoing issues, thus avoiding the unpleasant task of bothering their equally demanding boss.

Nick Naff was director of publicity and advertising, responsible for handling most of the Colonel's needs. In the summer of 1973, he had his hands full. The Colonel's latest "request" was a doozy: The King wanted his new grand piano delivered to his suite on the 26th floor. The instrument had arrived by truck, unscathed. Now the hotel had to get it up to his room.

"I'm the piano mover and I'm telling you, there's no way it's going to fit. It's not safe and it's not going to happen," John Jacobs said, shaking his head as he looked up at the ceiling of the Hilton freight elevator. He rocked back against the wall of the elevator, crossed his arms, and looked defiantly at Nick Naff. "I've been moving pianos for ten years and you just can't fit a large peg into a small hole. You're going to have to find another way to get it up there."

"Are you sure?" Nick groaned. "It has to be in Elvis's suite by tomorrow."

"Sorry. My company won't allow me to risk damaging a piano. Even if I take off the legs, it's too big to put in this elevator."

"Great," Nick mumbled to himself. He reluctantly made his way to the executive offices to tell Henri Lewin, a man who hated snags of any kind in his hotel, about the problem. He hoped Henri wouldn't blow a gasket, which he was often known to do.

Lewin rocked back in his big leather chair. He was tall and slender, but had a dominant presence. He was all business. At least everyone who worked with him thought so.

He eyeballed Nick from behind his glasses. "Look, Nick, if Elvis and the Colonel want a piano in the Imperial Suite, that's what they get. Do your job and call Ad-Art. They can haul it up there. That's what we bought a crane for." He dismissed Nick with an abrupt wave of his hand.

"Yes, Mr. Lewin." Nick left the office.

A few minutes later, Kent Carmichael came on the line. "What's up, Nick?"

"It's a big mess. Elvis wants his grand piano hauled up to the Imperial Suite for a big wing-ding he's throwing after his show tomorrow. The Colonel's having a fit about it and Henri's pissed about that. If I don't get the damn piano up there by tomorrow night, there'll be hell to pay. It weighs seven hundred pounds and it won't fit in the freight elevator. The piano mover flat-out refused to try. Henri said to call you. He said you could use the crane to lift it."

"Not possible and Henri knows it. He terminated monthly maintenance on the crane once the Hilton letters went up. It'll take at least three days to get it prepped for a lift like that."

Nick's voice lowered. "I really need you to come up with something, Kent. This party's a big deal and if Elvis doesn't get his piano, I doubt I'll have a job after tomorrow."

Kent sighed into the phone. "All right. Don't worry. Tell Henri I'm on my way. And don't let the piano guy go anywhere. I'll need to talk to him." Kent hung up the phone and headed for the warehouse. He found one of his workers, Ferrill Rushton, outside, loading up a maintenance truck. "Ferrill, whatever you're doing, drop it. I need you to come with me to the Hilton. Come on. I'll drive."

By the time they reached the Hilton, Kent had explained the problem and Ferrill had come up with a plan. With no crane available, Ferrill had suggested that a greenlee, a pulling tool that used rope to lift heavy objects, was the ticket.

"We just need to see the piano, and check out the roof to make sure our sandbags are still up there," Ferrill said. "I'm pretty sure a weighted-down greenlee can lift it."

"That's 300 feet, Ferrill. Will a greenlee do the trick?"

"Sure. We can rent one from Vegas Valley Electric that can lift seven hundred pounds, easy. Our problem is the rope. We don't have enough rope to do it."

"Ahern Rental might have three hundred feet of rope. I'll go over there and talk to Lois," Kent said. Ahern was the largest industrial rental company in Las Vegas. Ad-Art occasionally rented equipment for sign hanging when it was needed too infrequently to warrant purchase. "I'm pretty sure we can rent a strong nylon rope long enough for the job from her."

"Sounds like a plan, boss," Ferrill said, extinguishing his cigarette in the truck's ashtray as the vehicle rolled to a stop.

Kent parked the truck and the two men headed for Nick's office to explain the plan.

The walls of the entertainment-director's outer office were covered with autographed 8x10 photos of stars who had performed at the Hilton. Each framed glossy print featured a gold-engraved tag identifying the individuals in the photo, along with the date the photo was taken. The wall featured a who's who of famous celebrities, none bigger than Elvis himself.

Ferrill admired a photo of Nick standing next to Elvis in one photo. Nick was wearing a broad smile, teeth shining, as the two shook hands. But as he and Kent entered the inner office, Ferrill noticed Nick wasn't smiling.

Nick looked up at Kent with a sheepish expression on his face that pleaded for help. "Well?"

"Relax, Nick," Kent said. "We have a plan. I need to talk to the piano mover. Any idea where he went?"

Nick breathed a sigh of relief. He hadn't forgotten the stern look on Henri's face. A weak smile appeared on his own. "He's in the coffee shop. Should I go get him?"

"Not yet. Just make sure he doesn't run off on us."

Nick "Will do. Maybe I'm not going to lose my job after all."

Kent and Ferrill took the elevator to the roof. "I told you these sandbags would still be up here," Ferrill said, squinting in the sun as he pulled a cigarette from the pack he'd removed from his shirt sleeve. He lit the cigarette and began counting the sandbags lying in piles on the roof of the hotel. "I knew we left them here when we finished hanging the 'H.' Hell, these bags have been up here since this place was the International."

Kent walked over to the edge of the roof and looked down at the ground. Ferrill's plan was to hold down the greenlee with the sandbags and lift the piano from the parking lot up to the balcony of Elvis's suite. It was a long lift and men would have to be positioned every couple of floors to keep the piano from swinging into the side of the building.

Ferrill blew a smoke ring and walked over to stand beside Kent. "The piano mover can remove the legs, the pedals, and the lid. That'll lighten the load. We can wrap the piano, no problem."

Back at the warehouse, Kent sent Ferrill over to Vegas Valley Electrical to rent the greenlee, and then headed off to Ahern to talk to Lois, the owner of the business.

Lois greeted Kent from behind the counter as he entered the building. Kent explained what he needed and why.

"You're in luck," Lois said. "We just got in a roll of nylon rope and we haven't cut it into lengths yet. You can rent the whole roll if you want. It's gonna stretch, though. That's a lot of weight you'll be lifting."

Kent knew the rope would stretch and it had him worried. "Do you have the specs on this rope at three hundred feet of lift capability?"

"Let me get the shipping label." Lois rounded the counter and disappeared into the warehouse. She returned, manila envelope in hand. "The tensile strength at three hundred feet shows two thousand pounds. You're good to go."

"Great. I'll send the boys over to pick it up later today. We'll be done with it by tomorrow, one way or the other."

"It'll be waiting for them at the loading dock," she said. "Good luck tomorrow."

Just before dawn the following morning, Ferrill, Dick Kline, and Andy Lodwick parked the maintenance truck by the main freight elevator at the loading dock at the back of the Hilton, off Joe W. Brown Road. The three men unloaded the rented greenlee, the roll of nylon rope, and their toolboxes, and set them in the elevator. They rode the elevator to the roof in silence. The scheduled 5 a.m. meet-up at the warehouse was early.

"This is a lame-brain move, if you ask me," Dick said, holding on to one side of the greenlee. "I'm a sign man, not a piano mover."

"Correction, piano 'lifter,'" Ferrill said, grinning.

"Very funny. I bet this was your idea, wasn't it, Rushton?" Dick said in mock reprimand. The men had worked together for years in the sign business and the constant daily jabs were nothing more than thinly veiled expressions of affection. "Goddamned early to be 'lifting' a piano."

When the elevator stopped in the open air at the top of the hotel, the sun was just beginning to rise. The three men rolled the greenlee and the roll of rope toward the northeast side of the roof.

"This is good." Ferrill pointed to a spot not far from the edge. He looked down to see the balcony of the Imperial Suite directly below them. "Let's tie her off and weight her down."

While Andy set the roll of rope in position to be attached to the greenlee, Ferrill and Dick began securing the machine by lifting 100-pound bags of sand and dropping them on the legs extending from the greenlee base. Each bag dropped onto the roof with a loud thud.

"Let's take our time and use all twenty of them. This sucker's going to be lifting a lot of weight. We don't need her flying off the roof and killing someone."

Dick grabbed a sandbag and threw it over his shoulder. "No worries about that. Hell, we could wake the dead with all the noise we're making." He slammed another sandbag onto a leg of the greenlee.

Dick's comment was meant to be funny, but one floor below, a very angry Elvis was on the phone to security. "What the hell is going on up there on the roof? All that pounding woke me up. Sounds like a herd of buffalo up there."

"So sorry, Mr. Presley. We'll go up right now and find out what's going on." The rattled security guard looked at his fellow security guard and silently mouthed the words, "It's Elvis."

"You do that. Or I'll go up there and take care of it myself."

The security guard winced. Elvis was known for his fondness of guns. During an earlier engagement at the hotel, Elvis and his bodyguards had amused themselves by firing shots at the chandelier in the main salon of the suite. They were attempting to hit the crystal balls hanging from the chandelier, but only managed to lodge a spray of bullets in the ceiling. The suite was on the top floor and nobody got hurt, so management let it slide.

"No need, Mr. Presley," the guard said. "We're on it." The phone slammed down as he was speaking.

"Oh, crap. Elvis is pissed." He dropped the phone and ran out of the security office toward the service elevator.

Only a week before, an argument between Elvis and one of his bodyguards had resulted in two gunshots fired through the penthouse windows. The nerves of the security guards were on edge after seeing panes of shattered glass falling from the penthouse to the ground 30 floors below. The last thing the guards wanted was another incident involving Elvis on their shift.

The guard hit the button and rode the elevator to the roof. He found Ferrill and his men working away. "What are you guys doing up here?" he demanded. "Do you realize you just woke up Elvis Presley?"

"Well, someone has to lift Mr. Presley's fancy piano and you're looking at them," Ferrill said with a smirk. "Tell Elvis if he wants that grand piano in his suite… that one, down there," Ferrill pointed over the edge of the roof to the ground below, "he's going to have to deal with the noise. We'll be hoisting it up the side of the building and swinging it over the balcony. Probably gonna take all day." Ferrill shrugged and reached for another sand bag.

"Well," the security guard said. "Could you please do it quietly?"

Andy slapped the guard on the back. "Tell Elvis we're sorry. We're almost done here. We'll try to keep it down."

"Thanks." The guard retreated to the elevator and pushed the button to the casino floor. He crossed the casino and entered the switchboard operator's station. He asked her to find Nick Naff. "Let the public relations director deal with Elvis," he mumbled to himself. "Life's too short."

****

146

The Lift

Kent arrived at the Hilton a little before 9 a.m. He parked in the back of the hotel and headed toward the group assembled nearby.

The piano mover was busy re-checking the blankets wrapped around the piano, while Ferrill and four other Ad-Art crew members looked on.

"Hi, boss," Ferrill said as Kent approached.

"Hey, Ferrill. Boys." Kent saw the wrapped piano lid, legs, and pedals spread out on the ground. "Get a few of the guys to transport that stuff up to the Imperial Suite. They can use the freight elevator."

"You might want to wait a while on that, boss. We already got chewed out for making noise on the roof and waking Elvis." Ferrill let out a laugh. "Poor security guy who told us to quiet down just about wet himself over it. I guess Elvis was pretty pissed." Ferrill flashed a grin. "No pun intended."

"Just take them up and leave them with a security guard in the hallway until the lift's finished."

Jacobs gave him a reluctant nod. "It's your show now. I hope you know what you're doing."

Kent ignored the slight. "Tie it up, boys. Ferrill, you go back up to the roof with Andy and Dick. Signal down when you're ready and start the lift."

"You got it, boss."

"And Ferrill, start the lift slow. Let's see how the rope takes the weight."

While the three made their way to the roof, Kent directed the other crew members to accompany security guards standing by and take their first position on the second floor. "These guards will give you access to rooms on every other floor leading up to Elvis's suite."

The spotting procedure was unusual, but necessary. Lifting without a crane, the piano would pass precariously close to the side of the hotel. Crew members would access the balconies of each designated room and use guide lines attached to the piano to steady the lift and prevent it from swaying into the building. As the piano lifted, the men would alternate, moving two floors farther up to grab the lines from the men on the balcony two floors below.

Ferrill signaled down and the lift began. He and Dick started turning the greenlee.

The rope began to wind.

Five feet. Ten feet. Fifteen feet.

Andy looked over the side of the building. "It hasn't budged. The rope is stretching."

"Let's go a bit farther. It's bound to stretch a bit," Ferrill said.

Andy shook his head. "OK, but that's a lot of weight down there."

"You worry too much. Just keep watching."

Twenty feet. Twenty-five.

The reel of rope pulled through the greenlee. It reached thirty feet.

Then thirty-five.

Andy looked over the edge. The men on the ground stood beside the piano, holding onto motionless guide lines. Two heads peered out from a balcony on the second floor. The piano hadn't budged. "I don't like this, Ferrill. What if it breaks?"

"Fine. Let's hold it here, Dick. Andy, get on the walkie-talkie. Get Kent up here."

"Finally," Andy said, pulling his walkie-talkie from his belt.

"Kent, we're at nearly forty feet and the piano hasn't moved."

"I'm on my way up."

Kent stood beside Andy. He looked down from the roof of the Hilton at the piano resting 300 feet below. He tugged on the taut rope. "What do you think, Ferrill?"

"I think it's solid. We knew it would stretch."

"OK, go for it."

Ferrill and Dick resumed the pull while Kent stood by. "It'll hold. Keep going," he said.

After sixty feet of rope had pulled through the greenlee, the piano budged.

"It's finally lifting," Andy cried out.

Ferrill looked at Dick and grunted. "I knew it would hold." He called out to Kent, "Are the guys in place on the balconies?"

"Yes. Pull. Slowly, Ferrill."

The piano lifted at a snail's pace, inch by inch, foot by foot, floor by floor. Men stationed every two floors leaned over the balconies, passing the guide lines off until the piano hung in the air adjacent to a balcony on the twenty-fifth floor. The lift, up until that point, had taken six hours. "Stop the lift, Ferrill," Kent said. "Andy, you wait here by the edge. I'll signal you from Elvis's balcony when we're ready to resume."

Kent left the roof and headed for the Imperial Suite. Two of his crew members were waiting in the hall, along with the security guard who had been watching over the other piano parts resting at the entrance to the suite.

Kent approached them. "The piano's just below Elvis's balcony. Let's get in there."

The security guard took a deep breath and then buzzed the suite. He was the same guard who had spoken with an angry Elvis that morning. He'd been there all day and his shift wasn't over.

Elvis's bodyguards opened the door.

149

"These men are here to swing Elvis's piano into the suite from the balcony," the security guard said, looking up at the two giants towering over him.

"From where?" one bodyguard asked. "Did you say the balcony?"

"Yes." Kent stepped up and explained what was happening.

The bodyguard gave him a confused look. "Wait here." He walked over to the balcony and slid open one of the glass doors. "Holy crap, that's the boss's piano, all right," he said, peering down and spotting a quarter-ton of grand piano dangling in the air. "Let them come in," he said to the second bodyguard. "This I've got to see."

The bodyguards watched as Kent and his men opened the second sliding glass door to the balcony.

Kent called up to the roof for Andy.

Andy looked over the edge from the roof. "Ready, boss?"

"Yes. Tell Ferrill and Dick to take it real slow. I'll signal you when we have it in position to swing it in."

The piano slowly lifted up into position just above the rail of the balcony.

"Stop!" Kent yelled up.

Ferrill and Dick held the rope on the greenlee secure. Once the men in the suite had the guide lines, they began swinging the piano over the rail.

"Tell Ferrill to give me about five feet of slack, Andy. Real slow," Kent called up.

The piano was off the balcony and in the suite's main living room, still attached to ropes, when Elvis emerged from his bedroom. He stood before the men in a white Hilton bathrobe, looking through sleepy eyes. "What's going on in here?" he said, looking at the spectacle in front of him.

"It's your piano, boss," one bodyguard said as the crew balanced the piano in the air above the carpet. "Part of it, anyway."

A boyish smile appeared on Elvis's face. "So this is what all the noise has been about." He looked over at the security guard, then at Kent and his men. Elvis walked over to the open balcony doors and looked outside. "Is this how you got it up here?" he asked. "Who do I have to thank for this?"

The security guard pointed to Kent and his crew, all gathered around the piano. "These men have been working all day to get your piano up here."

"Yes, Mr. Presley," Kent said. "Sorry for the noise this morning, and for the inconvenience, but it's a big piano."

"Yes, it is. Where's the rest of it?"

"In the hall," the security guard said. "I've been guarding it all day. The piano mover's on his way to come up and reassemble it for you."

"Well, you all have my thanks. What can I do for you?" he asked.

The security guard took a timid step forward. "My wife would love an autograph, if you wouldn't mind."

Elvis went back into his bedroom and returned with a pile of autographed headshots. He handed them to the guard. "You see to it that everyone involved in this move gets one."

John Jacobs emerged from the elevator. He knocked on the door of the Imperial Suite and identified himself.

Kent's crew moved the remaining piano parts from the hall into the suite and placed them on the carpet beside the piano.

With John's guidance, the men worked together to reassemble the piano. John tuned it and 30 minutes later, a delighted Elvis sat playing his white grand piano

Later that night, high on the roof of the penthouse of the Hilton, some monkey business was afoot. The Imperial Suite below was alive with musicians, groupies, and a select group of friends of the famous entertainer, all gathered for the after-show party. Elvis's giant white grand piano rested in the center of the Imperial Suite's main living room, a testament to the ingenuity of the sign men who delivered it.

But a small group of drunken partiers had left the suite and made their way up onto the roof to gaze out on the famous Las Vegas Strip in all its glory.

"Look," one of the partiers said, staggering over to the sandbags. "Let's throw one off the roof and see where it lands."

The man leaned over and attempted to lift a bag. "Nah, these suckers are too heavy to throw anywhere."

However, years before, when the Hilton was still the International, someone had done just that.

****

The Sandbag Incident

Elvis was headlining at the hotel and living up to his "taking care of business" motto. One of his after-show parties was in full swing when a music program featuring Robert Goulet was airing on a television in the suite and drew the ire of the young star. "I can't stand that guy," Elvis said. He grabbed a handgun from his collection and fired directly at the image of Goulet onscreen, putting two bullet holes in the television and shattering it.

The party grew louder as the evening progressed into the wee hours of the morning, but Elvis's wild parties were simply accepted by management as part of the star's persona. After all, it was Elvis. He was making hundreds of thousands of dollars for the hotel. They could replace televisions. They couldn't replace Elvis.

The following morning around 8 a.m., Dan Celeste, Nick Naff, and Chris Karamanos were making their rounds outside the hotel and stopped abruptly when they reached the northeast corner of the parking lot.

"This is just great. What the hell is that? And how did it get on that Cadillac?" Dan said, shaking his head in disgust at the scene in front of him. The front hood of the Cadillac was completely crushed. A large canvas bag had landed just in front of the windshield.

The weight from the object had toppled the car forward off its rear tires. "It must have been a big impact," Nick said. "Look at that engine. It's on the ground, right next to the wheels."

They approached the vehicle to get a closer look.

"Man, look at the damage. Are those sandbags?" Nick pointed to some objects on the ground at the front of the vehicle.

"Yeah, and I have a pretty good idea where they came from," Dan said with a frown. The three men had been advised of gunfire in the Imperial Suite the night before by the head of security.

Dan wrenched his neck back to look up at the roof of the hotel. The balcony of the Imperial Suite was directly underneath. He shook his head and sighed. "It had to be some drunken clowns messing around on the roof last night. The big question is, whose car is it?"

Nick looked around at the other cars parked in the lot. They appeared unharmed. "Thank God it happened when nobody was out here. Someone could have been killed." He shuddered at the thought. "We got lucky, Dan."

Nick, Dan, and Chris walked around the Cadillac, examining the damage. "This car's totaled," Dan said. "The hotel will replace it, but we have to keep Elvis's name out of it."

The three men reentered the hotel and informed the hotel president, Alex Shoofey, of the problem. Together, they manufactured a story about a construction accident for the benefit of the local press and made arrangements to appease the owner with a new Cadillac. The man was delighted with the hotel's generous offer and what really happened to his Cadillac remained hush-hush.

After all, this was Las Vegas. And the later slogan popularized the notion that what happens in Vegas stays in Vegas.

****

The Colonel's Sole

December came and the Colonel arrived to spend the holidays gambling in the casino. It was a grueling time of year for all the hotel executives, with expectations for large casino profits high, and with Christmas over, Dan and all the other execs were relieved. If they could just get through New Year's Eve, things would slow down in January and everyone could get some well-deserved rest.

Dan answered the phone on the fifth ring. It was New Year's Day and he was wiped out from all the hotel activity the night before. "What is it? This is supposed to be my day off," he snapped at the caller on the other end of the phone.

"I'm sorry, Dan, but we've got a problem." The voice on the other end was Chris Karamonos. "I just got a call from the Colonel."

"What? Isn't he gone yet?" Colonel Parker was scheduled to fly out early that morning from Las Vegas to his home in Palm Springs. Dan had made all the necessary arrangements. "What's the problem?"

"He called from Palm Springs and he was pissed," Chris replied with a sigh. "He had a bad night in the casino and was already in a foul mood before he flew out. He said his shopping list wasn't complete."

Dan groaned. One of his many Colonel-related duties, completely set aside from anything involving Elvis, was to supervise the Colonel's culinary needs during his air travels leaving Las Vegas. Every time the Colonel checked out of the hotel, he supplied the food and beverage department with a shopping list of items to be loaded onto his jet. On occasion, Dan had to spend the better part of a day locating last-minute items added to the Colonel's list. "What's missing?"

"Whoever packaged the load forgot the Dover sole. I'm going to need you to fly down there and deliver him his fish."

"Today? Are you nuts?" Dan was livid. "I've got a date with Carolyn. It's my first day off in two weeks and I promised her we'd spend it together." His blood pressure skyrocketed at the thought of something so stupid screwing up his plans. "You can't be serious."

Chris was serious. "We've got a plane lined up for you. You've got to go over to the Bonanza Hotel. Go to the front desk and ask for Al Benedict. We're using his plane."

"Al Benedict? The Al Benedict who was just announced as president of MGM? That Al Benedict?"

"Yeah, that Al Benedict."

"Uh, OK." Dan's attitude suddenly improved. He was going to play delivery boy with a load of frozen fish in Al Benedict's private plane.

Dan drove to the Bonanza. The casino was quiet, with only a smattering of gamblers playing at the tables. He approached the front desk. "There should be a message for me from Mr. Benedict, regarding his plane," Dan began.

"Oh, yes, just a moment," the woman at the front desk replied.

Dan waited for a message to be delivered to him from Benedict's office. A few minutes later, Al Benedict himself came out to meet him.

He shook Dan's hand. "You must be Dan. I'm Al Benedict."

Dan grinned from ear to ear. This fish delivery had afforded him the opportunity to meet the new president of the MGM.

Benedict told Dan where to meet his pilot and where the plane was parked. Dan left the Bonanza, picked up his cargo packed in ice, and flew to Palm Springs.

The taxi pulled up to the Colonel's home and Dan got out, Dover sole in hand. He asked the taxi to wait. "I'll just deliver this package and head back to the plane."

He walked to the front door, rang the bell, and braced himself to face a fuming Colonel.

No answer.

He rang again.

Still no answer.

On the plane ride, Dan had rehearsed how he was going to tell Carolyn all about his VIP flight on the jet of the president of the MGM and how he had insisted on getting back in time for his date. If that didn't impress her, he figured nothing would. And now the Colonel was nowhere to be found.

He looked back at the waiting taxi. "The hell with it," he said under his breath. "This fish is on ice."

He left the package of Dover sole on the front porch, then flew back to Las Vegas and his dinner date with the woman who later became his wife. That night, he ordered Dover sole, which turned out to be Carolyn's favorite. When he told her the insane details of his impromptu trip to Palm Springs, she laughed. It turned out she was very understanding.

Although Dan stayed with the International through its transition into the Las Vegas Hilton, when the opportunity for advancement in his field emerged, he moved on. He interviewed at the MGM Grand with the vice-president of finance for a position as food and beverage controller. He landed the position and his first day on the job, he was introduced to the other executives. At one point, he found himself standing in front of Al Benedict.

A broad smile appeared on Benedict's face. "I remember you," he said. "You're the fish guy!"

13

Some Things Never Change

While Elvis and other headliners were packing main showrooms, lesser-known acts were entertaining in the numerous casino lounges, both downtown and on the Strip. During the '60s and early '70s in particular, lounges in Las Vegas were stepping stones to discovery and stardom for many up-and-coming performers.

Sets in the lounges ran into the early hours of the morning, with late-night crowds filtering in after main showroom performances ended. The music was loud and the comedy was blue, igniting booze-induced revelry that lasted until dawn. Management deliberately booked entertainers who could keep the energy and alcohol flowing. High-strung inebriated guests left the lounges and headed straight for the tables to gamble.

One of the most popular lounge entertainers of his day was Redd Fox. Before his success with "Sanford and Son," Redd frequently played the lounge at the International. He alternated with Kenny Rogers and the First Edition and Ike and Tina Turner, back when Ike, the act's headliner, was upstaged by Tina every night.

Of all the entertainers who performed in the lounge, Redd was best known for his raunchy language and his ever-present scotch. He drank it like water.

His love affair with whiskey was well-known among food and beverage people and Dan Celeste was no exception. It was Dan's job to keep Redd's hotel suite stocked with whatever the comedian desired, and JB Scotch topped the list. Dan didn't know whether it was consumed by Redd's entourage or Redd himself, but it went fast.

"Bring me another bottle of scotch, will you?" Redd called and asked Dan and a bottle magically appeared. Over the course of his numerous engagements at the International, Redd got to know Dan as the "scotch guy." Dan took it in stride.

Years passed and Dan moved on to the MGM Grand, where he held the title of Director of Services, in addition to his position as Food and Beverage Controller. He held these positions for nearly two decades.

Dan hadn't seen or heard from Redd in years, until one day he heard a familiar voice.

"Hey, Celeste, is that you?" Redd called out from outside the entrance of the MGM health spa.

One of Dan's responsibilities was overseeing the running of the hotel's spa. It was a high-end facility that catered to a sophisticated clientele. The voice calling out to him was hardly sophisticated. There was no mistaking who it was.

"Danny Celeste, how the f**k are you?" Redd called out as he walked into the spa.

Dan released a mildly embarrassed laugh as he looked around. People within earshot inside the spa were not taking kindly to Redd's colorful language.

There was no controlling the situation, so Dan just rolled with it. He greeted the comedian. "I'm doing fine, Redd. How've you been?"

Redd didn't skip a beat. "Everything's good. Hell, it's been a long time since the old days at the International. You must be the 'scotch guy' around this joint now. Get me another bottle of JB, will you?" he hollered, kidding with Dan as he passed by. "It's damned good to see you." He continued walking, waving behind his back as he entered the men's locker room.

Dan looked around at the crowd observing the scene, some whispering to one another as they watched Redd walk away. Dan just shrugged and shot the crowd a look that said, "Hey, it's Vegas."

Redd hadn't changed a bit and the encounter gave Dan an idea.

An hour later, Redd walked out of the spa to discover Dan standing by the entrance. Resting on the counter beside him was a bottle of JB.

"You crazy son of a bitch," Redd shouted. "Just like the good old days."

Dan smiled. Redd was one of a kind. He sure loved his scotch.

****

Because Khashoggi Wants It, That's Why

Of Dan's many responsibilities at the MGM, satisfying the demands of high rollers was paramount on the list. The massive amounts of money they gambled away entitled them to VIP privileges well out of reach of the average gambler. From the casino floor to the penthouse suites, hotel executives and employees alike catered to their every whim.

Nestled on the 26th floor of the MGM Grand was the Metro Club, designed exclusively to accommodate reclusive VIP guests and select high rollers. It was set up as a mini-casino, complete with slot machines, a 21 table, and a full-blown bar and gourmet restaurant.

Dan catered to the Metro Club's clientele on a routine basis. He worked in conjunction with the club's maître d' George LaForge, to ensure all services were performed to the satisfaction of the customers gambling there. Fine dining from the restaurant was available 24/7, with cocktail waitresses and bartenders serving players from the bar located adjacent to the gaming.

"What's up?" Dan asked, approaching George at the Metro Club bar. The call had come in to his office that George had a problem.

George stood at a little over six feet tall. His strong French features were highlighted by thick-black hair graying slightly at the temples of his tanned face. He had the robust build of a boxer. George was a mainstay at the hotel and an expert at his job. Accommodation was his strong suit and it served him well when dealing with the eccentricities of the hotel's most coveted guests.

"You're not going to like this one, Dan," George said, his voice ringing with a comical tone. "It's a doozy."

"Is that so?" Dan replied.

George's sense of humor when reacting to the many exorbitant demands of Metro Club gamblers, along with his charming accent, had endeared him to Dan. Nothing much fazed the man. In the casino business, a sense of humor often proved to be invaluable.

"I'm sure you know Khashoggi's flying in next week."

"Yes," Dan said, his eyebrows lifting slightly at the mention of Khashoggi's name.

Adnan Khashoggi was a very famous, notoriously private, Saudi billionaire. Some called him paranoid, but it wasn't far from the truth. He had parlayed his family oil fortune into international arms dealing and he traveled with understandable caution. When he left his multi-million-dollar yacht, *Nabila*, to travel to Las Vegas with a harem of beautiful women, his entourage also included an army of military-trained bodyguards.

"Plans are in place for his visit. What's the problem?"

"Well," George motioned to a table by one of the club's bay windows. Each featured views of the Las Vegas Strip in all its neon glory. "Let's sit down." George waved at a cocktail waitress as they took their seats, pointing to Dan and then himself, and flashing two fingers.

She knew the drill. Both men would have coffee. They were working and rarely drank anything else. She nodded and disappeared into the service area.

"OK, what gives?" Dan asked.

"Khashoggi wants a crap table up here. I guess the twenty-one table and slots aren't enough for him."

"What? Why, all of a sudden?" Of all the requests high rollers made, this one came from left field.

"He saw one of the new tables in the casino his last visit and asked me why there wasn't one up here. He implied he might gamble elsewhere if we couldn't accommodate him with a crap table in the Metro. I thought you should know."

"Can't we just have facilities haul one up? You know I'll approve anything you want to do up here."

George nodded. "I know that, Dan, and I already contacted John about it. They put the order in and planned on moving one up here early tomorrow morning at the end of graveyard shift. But I got a call late this afternoon from John. He's worried the thing won't fit into the elevator. In fact, he said he measured it and he's sure of it."

The cocktail waitress appeared with two coffees. She set them down and gave the men a warm smile before leaving the table.

"What time is this table supposed to go up tomorrow?" Dan asked.

"Five a.m."

Dan groaned. Another early morning. "I'll go down now and talk to John. We'll work it out. Any other problems?"

"No. Sorry to bother you with this one, but it's Khashoggi."

"That's what I'm here for." Dan took a sip of his coffee, rose from his chair, and headed for the facilities office.

The following morning, Dan stood near the open door of one of the hotel's public elevators. The crap-table move had caught a snag when John realized it was too large to navigate all the turns it would take to get it to the freight elevator on the main floor of the MGM. Fortunately, the casino was relatively quiet at 5 a.m.

Dan looked up at the ceiling of the elevator. "Will there be enough clearance once the ceiling panel's off the top of the cab?"

"I think so," John replied, straining at the waist as he and three other members of the facilities crew hoisted the elevator ceiling panel into the air. They tilted the panel to an angle, barely avoiding the guide cables, and lowered it into the elevator shaft, where four more men were waiting for it. "Watch the cables," John said as the weight of the roof transferred to the men in the elevator.

Dan stepped back to clear the way for the crew to remove the panel from the elevator. They carried it out into the foyer and set it behind a partially dismantled and wrapped crap table. The legs had already been covered and transported up to the Metro Club for reassembly once the table reached the top.

The plan was simple. The elevator would be lifted using the manual override by an operator at the elevator's control box. It would rise slowly, floor by floor, while the crew held the crap table on its side, all the way up to the

26th floor. John would remain on top of the elevator, dodging the moving cables and keeping the table from shifting in the car.

The crew on the ground, led by Bob, the hotel's assistant facilities chief, lifted the crap table, tilted it on its side, and placed it on a dolly.

Once inside the elevator, they tilted it back up to a vertical position. The top of the table protruded up nearly two feet beyond where the ceiling panel had been.

Bob strained his neck to look up at John. He held fast to the table, grasping the section protruding from the top of the elevator with one hand and using the other hand to steady himself against the side of the elevator car. "Start the lift."

The elevator slowly began to rise. John steadied the table top to keep it from hitting the floor beams on the side of the elevator shaft as the elevator slowly rose. The men in the elevator leaned their shoulders against the four sides of the elevator car and pushed against the table to keep it balanced on the dolly.

"This is nuts," Dan whispered to himself as he rode another elevator up to the Metro Club. He joined an equally nervous George at the top, and the two men waited.

Forty-five minutes and twenty-six floors later, the elevator reached the top. The door opened.

Dan breathed a sigh of relief. The crap table had arrived.

The crew rolled the table into the club and placed it in the area George designated. John dropped down from the top of the elevator and joined the others in the club.

The table was unwrapped and reassembled in less than thirty minutes.

Two weeks later, after Khashoggi's stay at the MGM ended, the crap table was disassembled. Once again, Dan and George stood by the elevator door at the entrance to the Metro Club and watched as it was loaded into the elevator and began the slow descent back to the main casino.

George turned to Dan, crossed his arms, and shrugged. "Hell of a thing we had to do to make one guy happy." He paused. A broad smile appeared on his face. "I guess what goes up must come down."

Dan laughed. A memory from his days at the Hilton suddenly flashed in his mind. A crap table was one thing. At least this time they didn't have to lift a grand piano.

14

Pot of Gold

Gambling is the lifeblood of Las Vegas. From the '40s to present day, everything else has been designed to function as window-dressing, created to entice gamblers into parting with their money. The beautiful women, lavish hotel rooms, opulent cuisine—all nothing more than a siren's call to play.

But at one hotel, the Hilton, in spite of all the planning, all the building, and all the oversight, money literally slipped, unnoticed, through the cracks.

Tourist season was in full force and piano virtuoso Liberace was headlining at the Hilton. Fans packed the showroom, flocking to the Entertainment Capital of the World to see the charismatic star perform. He was the epitome of an entertainer, mesmerizing his audiences with his flashy costumes and nimble fingers and fueling the fire for gamblers riding on a high after seeing the flamboyant performer onstage.

"Good luck at the tables," the maître-d's echoed as they ushered the audience out of the showroom.

Loud conversation filled the air as the crowd strolled out into the brilliantly lit casino. The ceiling sparkled like the rhinestones covering Liberace's piano as guests found themselves drawn to the gaming tables beckoning below. Each player was a potential winner filled with anticipation, certain that Liberace's magic fingers would parlay into good fortune.

As the endless lines of customers spilled out onto the casino floor, pit bosses greeted them with smiles. Dealers dressed in crisp white shirts and black satin vests stood at attention behind the tables, ready to deal what every player was sure to be his or her own winning hand.

Of the many gaming choices provided by the Hilton, none was more popular than the Pot of Gold silver dollar slot carousel. Strategically located at the center of the casino floor, the irresistible glow of a giant neon rainbow loomed over the carousel, luring eager players to try their luck. Two giant pots of gold rested on either end of a 40-foot-long structure. The pots were painted with ornate gold flake and featured cascades of glittering gold coins. The cascades originated from the sweeping neon rainbow arch that stretched overhead between the two pots, and overflowed to the machines below.

The carousel's main attraction featured two towering dollar progressives. They rested brightly lit on either end of the carousel, just under the two pots of gold.

The Pot of Gold earned its reputation as the most played of any dollar slot carousel on the Strip by delivering frequent payouts on the progressive machines. Running along the sides of the carousel, under the rainbow and between the two progressives, were two rows of additional dollar slot machines. They provided ample options for players too meek to risk it all on the high-stakes progressive slots. The greater the risk, the greater the payoff, and the carousel offered enough variety for everyone.

It was Saturday night and Liberace had once again filled the casino. The pit was packed and every machine at the carousel was occupied. The clanging of dollars falling into metal trays competed with the ringing of jackpot bells and spinning slot wheels. The racket echoed off the walls throughout the casino.

Victoria, a buxom young change girl with long blonde hair, patrolled a platform encased within the carousel and raised three feet above the floor, providing slot players with a titillating view of the young woman's tanned and shapely legs. Victoria's job was to provide change in the form of silver dollars to players seated along the carousel. Doing so required her to bend at the waist to deliver the coins, a gesture that ensured the player a full view of her ample breasts. Male players reached up to receive their change, while enjoying the visual fringe benefits provided by the Pot of Gold. Female players looked on, some smiling in amusement, others shaking their heads in disapproval.

Carousel play was in full swing when, without warning, half of the neon lights illuminating the Pot of Gold rainbow went dark. A pungent odor of tar began to fill the air, alarming both the players and the change girl walking the platform.

Gary, a regular player, crinkled his nose. "What's that smell, Victoria?"

"Beats me," she replied, tossing her mane of blonde hair over her shoulder. "It smells like something's burning. I'd better let a pit boss know." Victoria stepped down off the carousel platform and closed the door behind her. "Back in a flash."

She headed toward Vinnie, the pit boss working the blackjack tables. She stopped at the table a few feet away from him, bringing play to a virtual halt.

From the cigar stub clenched in his teeth to the three-piece Italian suit stretched over his short and stocky body, Vinnie was a living breathing caricature of an Italian mobster straight out of a *Godfather* movie.

"Hi, doll," he said. "What are you doing away from the Pots?"

Victoria pointed behind her at the carousel. "Half the rainbow just went out and there's a funny smell coming from under the platform, like something's burning. I figured I'd better let someone know."

Vinnie looked over at the carousel. He could immediately see that there was a problem requiring the attention of maintenance. "You go on back and move those players off the slots."

"OK, Vinnie, whatever you say." Victoria spun on her heels and headed back toward the Pot of Gold.

Vinnie picked up the phone. "Get me Frank, in maintenance."

Frank Williams was a long-time maintenance man at the hotel. He'd spent years working his way up the Hilton ladder, from basic maintenance to slots, and he'd just landed swing shift. After a year on graveyard shift, he was finally on a shift that enabled him to actually have breakfast in the morning.

When Vinnie explained what was going on with the neon at the Pot of Gold, Frank said, "I'll check it out." Frank knew every inch of the property, from the showroom to the penthouse suites, and he knew the departments responsible for maintaining each one. "Better hurry. I can smell it all the way over here in the pit," Vinnie said.

Frank left the maintenance office and headed for the carousel. He stopped in front of Victoria, who was standing a few yards from her spot on the platform. Frank's eyes dropped to the cleavage popping out of Victoria's top. "Hi, sweetheart."

"Hi, Frank," Victoria replied, smiling sweetly.

Frank blushed.

Victoria pretended not to notice. "My carousel's down."

"Let's take a look." Frank pulled his gaze from Victoria's cleavage and walked around the vacant carousel. "By the electrical smell and loss of power to the neon, it's got to be a transformer," Frank said to himself. When it came to serious issues with hotel signage, if he couldn't fix it, he knew to follow protocol and call the company that built and maintained it. Everyone on the hotel maintenance crew knew better than to try to make repairs and jeopardize an outside maintenance contract. "I'm afraid you're done for the night, doll. I'm going to have to call someone from the outside."

Victoria flashed a huge smile at Frank. An "early out" meant an unexpected night off. Paul Anka had recently opened Jubilation, a disco club on Harmon Boulevard, a few blocks east, off the Strip. It was the most popular nightspot in Las Vegas for locals and tourists alike. "I think I'll call a girlfriend and go out dancing."

"Enjoy your night off, sweetheart," Frank said, as Victoria headed toward human resources to punch out. "Pretty little thing," he muttered under his breath.

She waved behind her head as she trotted away, making her breasts jiggle and grabbing the attention of more gawking onlookers.

Frank headed for the breaker panel that serviced the Pot of Gold Carousel. He switched off the breakers, returned to his office, and called Kent Carmichael, who had moved on from Ad-Art and was now manager at Heath Sign Company. Frank identified himself. "Sorry to call you at home, but half the rainbow's gone dark on the Pot of Gold. I think we've got a blown transformer. Can you send someone over tonight?"

Kent looked at his watch. It was close to 8 p.m. "No problem. I'll get night maintenance over there. Are the breakers off?" Kent knew Frank was a professional and had certainly turned them off. But it was Heath policy to ask, just in case.

Mild laughter filtered across the phone line from the other end. "What do you think? Yeah, I shut the whole thing down."

"Of course you did, Frank. I'll dispatch one of my guys over to you right away."

Kent reached across his couch to the pager on the coffee table and paged Ferrill Rushton, who also moved over to Heath when Kent did and was the man on crew duty that night. When Ferrill called in, Kent could hear music in the background. Wherever Ferrill was hanging out, he was free to go about his business, as long as he responded to his pager when a call came in. "Ferrill, I need you to go to the Hilton and check on the Pot of Gold neon."

"Sure, boss. What's the problem?"

Kent explained the situation. "Frank will unlock the maintenance door for you. Call me after you know what the problem is." He hung up.

"Duty calls," Ferrill said, chugging what was left of his beer. He rose from his chair at the Riviera sports book and headed for the company maintenance truck he'd left in the parking lot. Fifteen minutes later, he entered the slot maintenance room at the Hilton.

Frank was leaning over the back of a slot machine, screwdriver in hand. He heard the door open and looked up. "Hi, Ferrill. Thanks for coming."

Ferrill was a lanky man with a weathered face and ice blue eyes. His lean physique served him well in his early years as a sign hanger, but as time passed, sign maintenance proved to be much kinder to his aging body. He'd responded to more than a few maintenance calls over the years.

171

Frank set his screwdriver down. He pulled the side drawer of his desk open and retrieved a large set of keys. "Looks like a transformer blew, but you can see for yourself." The two men chatted as they walked down the hall toward the casino and the carousel.

Ferrill neared the carousel and detected the distinct odor of burning tar. "Whoa, yeah, that's not good."

Frank opened the maintenance access door at the back of the carousel.

Ferrill dropped to his knees to look inside. He crawled in just far enough to shine his flashlight toward the left end of the corridor. The light shone down the length of a 20-foot run, three feet high by ten feet wide. The transformer box was located behind the progressive machine at the far end.

"Holy shit," he whispered to himself.

An enormous mound of silver dollars was piled up at the end of the corridor. The pile, glittering from the flashlight, rose more than three feet high from the floor all the way up to the basket of the big progressive machine on the end, and beyond, to the adjacent slots on either side. The coins had spilled out in a blanket of silver, stretching several feet down the corridor toward him.

"How the hell did that happen?" he said under his breath. He turned his flashlight to the opposite end of the slot corridor to check on the remaining dollar machines.

Nothing.

It appeared the discovery was limited to one machine at one end, at least.

Ferrill turned off his flashlight, crawled out of the corridor, and closed the maintenance door. Frank had wandered away and was engaged in conversation with Vinnie.

"Frank," Ferrill waved over at the two men.

172

Frank walked back to join Ferrill.

"You can close her up. I have to go back to the warehouse and get some equipment. I'll find you when I get back. Shouldn't take long."

Frank locked the door.

Instead of heading for the truck, Ferrill walked across the casino floor directly to the casino house phones located by the front desk. He called Kent. "Boss, we've got one hell of a problem here." He explained what he'd discovered. "Somehow a whole bunch of silver dollars have buried our transformer. I don't know how it managed to work as long as it did with all that weight on it. It had to be ripped right off the platform. There's no way to get to it. It's buried under a mountain of money."

"What?" Kent asked. "That doesn't make sense." The slot barrels were emptied every shift. "How much?"

"A lot. You have to see it to believe it."

"OK, Ferrill, you're finished there. I'll take it from here. And Ferrill, you didn't see anything in there, OK? Keep this between the two of us for the time being."

"You got it, boss. I didn't see a thing."

"Hold on a minute, Ferrill. You didn't by any chance crawl inside and personally check out that mound of money, did you?"

The question brought a smile to Ferrill's face. "No, I was a good boy." Management at the Hilton had several not-so-subtle ways of dealing with anyone caught stealing from the casino. Ferrill valued his knees and knuckles. Pinching a few silver dollars just wasn't worth the risk. "I promise. They're all still there."

"Good." Kent hung up the phone and dialed the Hilton.

"Las Vegas Hilton, what extension please?"

"Howie Merhar in slots."

"One moment, please."

Howie Merhar worked as slot-maintenance manager at the Hilton. Frank, as well as all the other slot mechanics, answered to Howie. Kent had known him since way back to Howie's days as a simple slot mechanic.

After a short pause on hold, the operator returned to the line. "Mr. Carmichael, I've located Mr. Merhar. He's off property. He asked me to give you his number. He's expecting your call." She gave Howie's home phone number to Kent. Kent hung up and dialed the number.

"Howie here."

"Howie, it's Kent. I just talked to my man on night maintenance. We have a problem with the Pot of Gold. Can you meet me at the casino house phones in, say, twenty minutes? We need to see what's happened for ourselves. It could be a sensitive matter."

An hour later, Kent and Howie sat in the Hilton's coffee shop.

"I just don't understand how the slot crew could've missed it," Howie said. "There must be thousands of silver dollars dropped down inside that corridor. That mound was huge."

Howie stared down at the cold cup of coffee on the table in front of him. They'd been discussing the carousel problem for a half-hour and he hadn't touched his coffee. "What am I going to tell the brass? It must've taken months for that much money to slip down through those boards." Beads of sweat covered his forehead. He looked up at Kent with an expression that said it all. "What if they think I've been stealing from the casino?"

There was nearly constant play at both progressive machines and the barrels were overflowing most of the time and emptied regularly. At first glance, it was hard for either man to imagine how so many coins could fall through the spaces in the flooring unnoticed.

Upon closer inspection with a flashlight, Kent and Howie had discovered the problem. Gaping holes had formed on either side of the progressive's interior walls. The flooring had simply collapsed under the weight of the coins as they piled onto the boards. Logic dictated it had to have been happening for some time. There were just too many coins in the pile.

Heads were going to roll for this and, unfortunately for Howie, his was probably the first to go on the chopping block.

Kent leaned in toward Howie. "Your guys are going to have to go in there and get it out before we can replace our transformer. You saw for yourself. It's buried."

Howie gulped. "Kent, I don't trust my crew to do it. Word of what's happened would be all over the casino in a flash. Can't your guys do it?"

"Whoa, Howie." Kent threw his arms up and pulled back in his chair. "That's casino money you're asking us to handle. You need to talk to management before either of us does anything."

Howie took a sip of cold coffee. His hands were shaking. "Oh, God. What am I going to tell them?"

"I have an idea," Kent said. "It's a little unconventional, but it just might work."

Kent and Howie sat in the coffee shop for another hour hatching a plan. The idea was unorthodox at best, but Howie was willing to try anything. "You think your guys can pull it off?"

Kent shrugged. "Hey, it's better than no plan at all."

"I'll call an emergency meeting for tomorrow morning with the executives." Howie paused. His stomach was churning at the thought of facing the bosses. "I'll call you tomorrow after the meeting. Will you be available?"

"Sure, Howie, anything you need. Good luck tomorrow."

"Thanks." Howie rose from his chair.

Kent took a sip of his fourth cup of coffee. "What I'd give to be fly on the wall at that meeting," he said to himself as he watched Howie leave the coffee shop.

****

Howie Survives Henri

Howie tossed and turned in his bed, agonizing over the reaction the plan was going to bring. He rehearsed it over and over, silently and out loud. He'd learned over the years that there was nothing worse than facing the big boys with bad news about money.

"Just stay calm," he whispered to himself as he sat in the conference room of the executive offices, waiting for the arrival of the top bosses. His phone calls the night before had generated the expected livid reaction from several of the suits. He'd explained the discovery as best he could and fielded a barrage of questions, most of which he couldn't answer. Once the fireworks had died down, he managed to convince most of them that there was a solution to the problem, which he'd explain in detail at the meeting the following morning. He prayed that the plan he and Kent had come up with would pacify them.

Shortly after 9 a.m., the conference door swung open. Henri Lewin, president of the Hilton, arrived first. He was dressed for golf in a polo shirt and gray khaki pants. He glared at Howie and said nothing as he sat down at the opposite side of the conference table. Howie's knees bounced under the table. Sweat was already forming on his temples. He could feel Mr. Lewin's eyes on him, but dared not look up. A few minutes later, the door opened again. John Fitzgerald, the vice-president, entered, followed by Barron Hilton himself.

"How the hell could this have happened?" Fitzgerald began, his enormous frame towering over Howie as he rounded behind him and took a seat. "Money like that doesn't just fall through the cracks."

"Let's concentrate on solving the problem," Barron said as he took his seat at the head of the table. He gave Howie an encouraging nod.

"Damned well better come up with something," Henri snapped. He tugged at the collar of this golf shirt. The expression on his face spoke volumes. It was Sunday morning and his golf bag was waiting.

"You said you have a solution to this problem. Let's hear the plan." Barron said. As owner of Hilton Hotels, Barron Hilton was powerful. But he was also reasonable. He put both elbows on the armrests of his chair and leaned back. He rested his hands, fingers laced together in his lap. "How are you going to get all that money out of there without drawing attention to it?"

John Fitzgerald grunted. "That's one hell of a good question."

Henri Lewin sat staring at Howie with a scowl on his face, but said nothing.

Howie placed both hands on his knees to stop their bouncing under the table. "There's a way to get it all out, safely and unnoticed."

"This should be good," Fitzgerald said, rolling his eyes. "Let's have it."

Thirty minutes later, Howie sat once again alone in the conference room. He'd explained the plan he and Kent had come up with. It was met with mixed reaction. Henri

Lewin left for his golf date five minutes into Howie's explanation, shaking his head at what he called a "lame-brained idea." Barron Hilton listened patiently as Howie described the proposed plan in detail. Ultimately, Barron gave his OK.

Howie had breathed a sigh of relief as he watched Hilton and Fitzgerald leave the conference room. They were going along with the plan and, for the time being anyway, his head was still attached to his shoulders.

****

Ex-Bank Robber Gets His Hands on $2 Million

Kent assigned his three favorite men from the Heath maintenance team to execute the plan. Dick and Andy had left Ad-Art, along with Ferrill, and signed on with Heath when Kent moved on.

When they arrived at the warehouse to load the truck and prepare for their first shift at the Hilton, it was a little before 10 p.m. Andy eyeballed the huge toolboxes resting on the table beside power drills, rolls of cable, electric fans, and other equipment. "Those boxes are huge," he said, shaking his head. "I've never seen toolboxes that big."

Woody, a tall black man with arms the size of tree trunks, stood by the table. He was a skilled welder who took pride in his work. "I made them up myself this afternoon. Boss said he wanted them oversized." Normal toolboxes measured on average two feet in length, with a width of ten to twelve inches. The boxes Woody had built were over three feet long and twenty inches wide. Woody reached out for one of the toolboxes and grabbed the steel handles bolted to either side. "I gave you guys plenty of grip so you'll have some leverage to lift them. Boss says they're going to be heavy once you get them filled." He gave Kent a quizzical look. "What's going in these, anyway?"

"Sorry, Woody," Kent said. "Wish I could tell you, but I can't."

Woody flashed a smile, revealing a mouthful of shiny white teeth. "Well, I painted them and banged them up like you said." He set down the tool box and pulled out the hammer hanging off his tool belt. "Used this," he said. "Don't know why you wanted them to look so beat up, though."

Kent ignored the comment. Shiny new toolboxes were sure to draw attention. The older they looked, the less conspicuous they would be. He turned to Andy, Ferrill, and Dick. "This is going to be a tricky thing to pull off. I expect you guys to keep your heads down and your mouths shut."

The three men promised to follow all his instructions exactly. They packed up their maintenance truck and headed out. They arrived at the Hilton a little before midnight and parked in front of the Hilton loading area.

Andy retrieved a large slot machine cart from outside the entrance of the loading dock and rolled it to the back of the maintenance truck. It was mid-June and the 105-degree temperature recorded at its afternoon peak had cooled to 101 degrees. It was dry and windy.

"It could be worse," Andy said. "We could be carting all this stuff in the daytime. At least the sun's down."

"Yeah, right," Dick replied. "It's a regular spring breeze we got going on here." He dropped the back gate of the truck.

The three men unloaded the four oversized toolboxes, several transformers, two rolls of plexi sheeting, and a variety of power tools and wiring, then closed up the bed of the truck and rolled the cart to the security window at the loading-dock entrance.

The security guard on duty was sitting behind the window, eating a sandwich. Mustard had dropped onto his shirt above his belly, just under a nametag identifying him as "G. Grimes." He eyeballed the three men as they wheeled the cart through the double doors.

"Maintenance crew from Heath," Andy said with a wave as they passed by. "Frank in slots has our work order."

The guard continued chewing on his sandwich and silently nodded them through with a toss of his head.

The men pushed the cart through security toward the casino.

Security cameras, placed strategically along the hallway leading from the security window into the casino, monitored all movement. All employees were aware of their existence.

"We're being watched, boys," Ferrill warned under his breath as they made their way to the Pot of Gold. As outside employees, since they didn't answer directly to the casino bosses, they experienced extra scrutiny by casino security, like all outside maintenance crews. "Nothing to see right now, but I bet we're frisked before we leave." He pretended to shudder in fear.

Dick gave Ferrill a hearty slug to the shoulder. "It's not funny, Ferrill. I'm not nuts about touching all this money. I can't believe the boss came up with such a crazy plan."

"I can," Andy said. "It makes sense."

The plan was already set in motion. Frank had informed security, and some of his crew, that maintenance from Heath would be doing a complete overhaul of the electrical system running the carousel. Repair and replacement of all working parts could take several weeks, so the men would work during graveyard shift to minimize loss of revenue from the carousel.

Kent had warned his crew. "The graveyard pit bosses know what you're really doing. They'll control any curiosity that arises in the casino. You guys just crawl inside and pretend to be making repairs and replacing equipment. Try to work as quietly and quickly as you can."

He'd instructed the three to fill the toolboxes with money, pull them out of the corridor, and place them on the cart. After pushing the cart through the casino to the hallway, they'd be met by two casino security guards and escorted to the slot maintenance room. They would wait while the security guards unloaded the toolboxes and carried them into the maintenance room to be emptied. The empty toolboxes would then be returned to the cart to be refilled.

"You know how heavy these suckers are going to be once we get them loaded full of silver dollars?" Dick complained. "Hell, it'll take two of us just to drag the damned things the twenty feet from the pile to the maintenance door."

Ferrill walked between the two men, pushing the loaded cart from the back. "It'll take time to fill 'em up. We'll probably only have to do it a couple of times a shift. I wonder how many nights it's gonna take to get it all out of there."

"Beats me," Andy said. "But it's what the boss wants."

Frank was waiting at the Pot when the three men arrived with the cart. "I got the door opened for you guys." He leaned in to the men and lowered his voice, "Howie's filled me in on what you're really doing. I'll be standing by if you need anything."

181

Ferrill winked at Dick. Their work shift would last until 6 a.m., and then most of the carousel would reopen for play. Few would know what was really going on.

Kent's instructions had been clear. Andy would stay just inside the maintenance door opening to prevent anyone from looking inside. Ferrill and Dick would crawl down the three-foot-tall corridor to the mound of dollars, taking the empty toolboxes with them. Once all four boxes were filled with silver dollars, they would drag them, one by one, down the plexi sheeting they would place on the carpet leading back to the maintenance door. The boxes were going to be heavy and the plexi would allow them to slide along the carpet with a little less resistance. The corridor was confining and the work was going to be strenuous.

Ferrill crawled through the open door into the corridor and looked up from inside the opening at Andy. "Hand me a roll of that sheeting." Ferrill turned on this flashlight and set it on the floor, illuminating the path ahead. He crawled along the 20 feet of corridor, unrolling the plexi behind him.

Once he'd reached the mound of money, he flipped on the light switch on the side panel to his left. During the original construction of the Pot of Gold, house electricians had installed two electrical outlets and two working lights for use during maintenance or repair of the neon rainbow.

Andy and Dick unloaded the toolboxes and the rest of the supplies, and then crawled in to join Ferrill. Andy sat on the carpet, just inside the maintenance door opening. "You boys have a nice time, now," he joked. "I'll be here keeping guard."

"Very funny," Dick said. He began crawling toward Ferrill at the far end of the carousel, pulling a toolbox beside him.

The work lights illuminated the area containing the mountain of silver dollars and adjacent slot machines. Ventilation was minimal, with circulation limited to air filtering in from the open maintenance door.

"Dick, go back and get Andy to pull those two fans off the cart. It's gonna get hot in here quick," Ferrill said. His shirt was already sticky with sweat.

Dick crawled back down the corridor to the entrance and retrieved the fans. Once the fans were plugged in and blowing, he and Ferrill placed two of the four toolboxes in front of the big pile and started filling them. They stacked coins side by side in rows, rising to the top of the boxes.

"This is a shitload of dough," Ferrill said, wiping his face with the sleeve of his shirt. "Two boxes filled and we haven't made even a dent in that pile." He looked at Dick. "We're going to be here forever."

An hour later, Ferrill and Dick finished filling the four boxes.

"It's a damned good thing Woody bolted handles on the sides of these suckers," Dick said, straining on his hands and knees as they dragged the first tool box along the plexi sheeting toward Andy.

Ferrill said nothing. They were strong men and it was all part of the job.

One by one, they dragged the boxes outside the maintenance door to the waiting cart. The muscles in their arms bulged as they grasped the handles and lifted the boxes from the floor. Ferrill tossed Dick a grin of satisfaction, acknowledging the fact that not many men could lift that much weight. After they loaded the toolboxes onto the cart, the men covered them with enough miscellaneous items to disguise them. They'd been instructed to be as discreet as possible when moving the loaded toolboxes.

"Round one nearly complete," Ferrill said.

Andy stayed behind, while Ferrill and Dick pushed the loaded cart back up the route to the slot maintenance door. Once they made it to the corridor leading out of the casino, they stopped. Armed security guards joined them and escorted them down the long hallway, past the executive offices to the slot maintenance room.

Ferrill and Dick stood by while the guards removed the toolboxes from the cart and entered the maintenance room. The two men watched the guards struggle with the weight of the boxes.

"Big bad security guards, my ass," Ferrill said, shaking his head. "See how much trouble they had lifting those boxes? Hell, they wouldn't last a day on a sign hang."

Dick leaned against the hallway wall. "Nobody'll ever believe all this cloak and dagger stuff." He reached for a pack of cigarettes inside his shirt pocket. He pulled out a cigarette from the pack and offered the pack to Ferrill.

Ferrill took a cigarette from the pack, pulled out a lighter from his jeans, and lit both. "Nobody'll ever know." He took a drag of his cigarette and smiled at Dick. "Imagine if we ever tried to tell our grandkids about this somewhere down the line," he said. "They'd think it was just a tall tale told by grandpa."

Thirty minutes later, the guards emerged from the room, empty toolboxes in hand. Ferrill and Dick placed them back on the cart, covered them up, and headed down the hall toward the loading dock.

A blast of hot air hit them as they passed the security window and rolled the cart out the door. All three men had complained about the next part of the plan. They saw no need to return to the truck, but the boss believed in misdirection. Kent said it had to look like they needed more equipment to make repairs on the Pot. Nobody could know what they were really doing.

"Did you see the looks we were getting from those security guards?" Ferrill asked as they made their way to the truck.

"Yeah," Dick replied. "Makes me nervous." He'd noticed the many security cameras located throughout the casino. The eyes in the sky were everywhere. "Let's get back to Andy. It's his turn to crawl down to that pile of dough."

Dick and Ferrill returned to the carousel. The three men repeated loading the toolboxes two more times that night, finishing the first night's activities at 6 a.m. Each man had taken a turn at standing guard.

The trio continued working on the mound of money from the carousel for two weeks. As they cleared the coins, they discovered what had happened to the rainbow.

The silver dollars had buried the transformer, ripping it from its bolts. The wiring had stretched so far it had finally snapped clean, shorting out the transformer and shutting off the neon. The shorted-out transformer heated up, melting the hardened tar encasing it and causing the unpleasant smell that had alarmed Victoria and Gary. Seeing the broken unit, they all agreed that the original transformer continuing to function as long as it did under the weight of the coins was a blasted miracle.

Each toolbox housed five thousand coins. Three trips a shift with four toolboxes each trip totaled $60,000, every night, night after night. The rainbow continued to remain dark, but the carousel was reopened at 7 a.m. every morning and stayed open until just before the crew arrived at night. Only the one progressive machine and two-dollar slots on each side of the progressive were shut down during the "repairs."

Ferrill, Dick, and Andy replaced the transformer after they repaired the fallen flooring. Finally, they finished the job and no one in the casino, except the suits, a few security guards, and the graveyard pit bosses, were any wiser.

As a trusted employee, Frank had been placed back on graveyard for the duration of the Pot of Gold episode. Shortly after 6 a.m. on the morning of the crew's last night on the job, he turned the breakers back on and the rainbow was once again illuminated. "Thank God it's over," he muttered to himself. "I almost forgot how much I hated graveyard."

On the last day of the Pot of Gold adventure, Ferrill, Andy, and Dick stood in front of the security window, arms in the air, being searched for the last time. Every morning the ritual had been the same. Each man emptied his pockets before being frisked by one of the security guards on duty. Andy chuckled at the sight of Dick rolling his eyes and moaning in mock delight as an overweight middle-aged guard checked for hidden silver coins. He considered teasing his friend, but thought better of it. Dick's life as a safecracker was long over and his fellow workers had learned that bringing up his glory days on the wrong side of the law was unwise. The Barney Fife types in security wouldn't find it funny and Dick probably wouldn't either.

Every morning, Ferrill pretended to be ticklish, giggling as the guard slid his hands down his inner pants legs. Andy mimicked Ferrill's giggles, annoying the security guards and amusing the hell out of Ferrill and Dick.

Ferrill turned to his two buddies as they walked out into the bright sunlight and back to the truck. "What do you say to a few beers?"

"I think that sounds like a great idea," Andy replied. "This job's finally done. Let's celebrate."

They hopped in the truck, with Andy in the driver's seat. He drove down Sahara Avenue toward Foxy's.

Ferrill sat sandwiched between Andy and Dick, wearing a huge grin, his blue eyes twinkling. "I still think you guys should've let me bring in my toolbox. Those guards never once checked the transformer boxes. My box would've fit like a glove inside one of them. We could've filled that sucker up."

"Sure, Ferrill," Andy replied. "And all three of us could've ended up wearing cement shoes at the bottom of Lake Mead."

They all laughed.

In total, Ferrill, Dick, and Andy retrieved nearly two million dollars in silver from the Pot of Gold.

Dick looked out the window at the palm trees lining the street. The past few weeks had brought back memories. He'd never had his hands on anywhere near that kind of money during his safecracking days. It would've been Dick's biggest heist by far.

Too bad this time it had all stayed in the casino.

15

A Flood of Water Against a Flood of Lawyers

Money is the name of the game in Las Vegas. And where there's a lot of money at stake, there are attorneys. From the conviction and incarceration of mobsters like Benny Binion to the lawsuit filed by Ed Levinson against the FBI for wiretapping his office, attorneys have always been on the scene—negotiating, litigating, collecting fees.

Over the years, lawsuits against casinos have ranged from minor slips and falls to multi-million-dollar class-action suits for damages caused by fire, flood, injury, and loss of life. Casinos retained high-priced attorneys to protect their millions when lawsuits filed against them threatened serious financial loss, even potential bankruptcy.

In the years that followed his work for the Boys Club organization, Jerry Gillock went on to earn his law degree. His legal career advanced rapidly and he became one of the most sought-after legal professionals in the city, litigating some of the biggest cases in Las Vegas history. One such case occurred in the summer of 1975.

On the Fourth of July holiday weekend that year, one of the most significant flash floods ever to occur in Las Vegas inundated the Strip. It was famously referred to as the Caesars Palace Flood, since the devastation most often associated with it took place in Caesars parking lot. Also called the "hundred-year flood," it inundated upwards of 700 cars in the lot when floodwaters overwhelmed the patchwork system of flood control. The total damage caused by the flood was estimated at $4.5 million.

Inevitably, lawsuits charging Caesars Palace with liability over lost and damaged property ensued.

A few months after the flood waters subsided, Kent Carmichael got a call from Jerry Gillock.

Jerry and Kent had become friends when they teamed up to build the first Entertainers Hall of Fame in Las Vegas. It was located on the second floor of the Tropicana Hotel, adjacent to the *Les Folies Bergere* showroom. The museum failed for a number of reasons. Still, the friendship between the two men grew.

"Kent, if you can make it, come down to the courthouse tomorrow morning. I'm defending a case."

"That's an unusual request, coming from you," Kent said. "But I've always wanted to see you in action."

Jerry laughed. He was well-known as a colorful character with a reputation as an accomplished litigator. "I think you'll find it entertaining."

"Sounds intriguing. I'm game."

"Great. Just come to courtroom Number Eight, a little before nine o'clock, and take a seat."

The following morning, Kent arrived at the courthouse. He made his way to the courtroom chamber and looked around.

A row of several dozen Ivy League attorneys sat gathered in the courtroom at a long table, shuffling through folders and open briefcases. The sheer size of the group assembled there was enough to intimidate anyone.

Kent observed stern looks on the faces of the attorneys huddled together in quiet conversation. "If Jerry's going to take on all these defense attorneys single-handedly, it'll be a clear case of David vs Goliath," he said, shaking his head in apprehension as he passed behind the somber group.

Kent looked around for Jerry, but didn't see him. He found a seat next to a mutual friend of his and Jerry's and sat down in the front row. "I don't see Jerry anywhere," he commented as he took his seat. "Have you seen him?"

"He's right there, in front of you," the friend replied, pointing to a man seated at the defense table nearby, directly in front of their location.

"That's Jerry?" Kent said. The man looked nothing like the Jerry he knew. Jerry was a sharp dresser. He was a good-looking man with a full head of hair and a larger-than-life personality. The man in front of Kent was wearing a Sears and Roebuck tweed suit and sported black thick-rimmed glasses. His hair was slicked back in a conservative style. He looked like Buddy Holly in a business suit.

Kent called out, "Jerry?"

The man turned around, waved, got up, and approached Kent. "Glad you could make it." Jerry observed the confused look on his friend's face. "I know, not what you expected," he added, grinning.

Kent shook his head. "I didn't recognize you. This is a … different look for you." He gestured to Jerry's suit and glasses. "What's this all about?"

Jerry laughed. "I'm defending Caesars against liability in these flood damage cases. Just watch. There's a method to my madness."

At that moment, the judge entered the courtroom.

"Showtime," Jerry said with a wink.

The assembled group rose for the judge and, after preliminary procedures, the litigation began.

One by one, attorneys representing prominent insurance companies presented their cases. They strutted in their expensive Fifth Avenue suits, damning Caesars Palace for its "negligence and blatant failure" to protect the property of their clients that had been destroyed in the waters that engulfed the Caesars Palace parking lot during the flood.

"Cars parked in the Caesars Palace lot were inundated by floodwaters," one attorney began, pointing directly at Jerry's table. "And no one notified your client's guests so they could move their vehicles to safety."

"It was a wall of water," another attorney argued. "And Caesars did nothing to remove those cars."

"This casino cared more about keeping gamblers at its tables than it did about their customers' possessions," another insisted.

One attorney representing a man who had lost his brand-new Cadillac recreated the chaos of the event to make his case. "When debris-filled water slammed into my client's car and destroyed it, he was inside the casino. When the force of the rampaging water swept cars off the ground, literally creating hundreds of runaway boats, no one bothered to tell my client so he could rescue his valuable car and move it to safety. Caesars did nothing to inform the unfortunate owners of all those vehicles so they could move their cars."

Kent watched Jerry keep his cool as the line of attorneys stepped up, one by one, to make their case. They all claimed that Caesars Palace was liable for all the damage caused to the affected vehicles, thus freeing the insurance companies that they represented of any financial liability. It all rested, they said, on Caesars Palace.

Finally, it was Jerry's turn. He stood alone, looking mild-mannered and unintimidating in his $27 Sears and Roebuck suit. He pushed his glasses up his nose and began his defense. "Yes, it's true that many vehicles suffered significant damage. That is unfortunate. However, allow me

191

to make a few statements that I believe will fully exonerate my client."

Jerry paced gracefully in front of his desk, addressing the judge and casually acknowledging the slew of men who had moments before attempted to skewer Caesars Palace with lightning-bolt accusations of incompetence and greed.

"None of the gentlemen here today condemning Caesars Palace have bothered to mention the fact that all the owners of the cars parked in the lot ignored clearly posted 'No Parking' signs that warned of a flood threat in that restricted parking area. In addition, it's a fact that after the initial completion of the blacktopping of the parking area, Caesars Palace hired a gentleman named Paul Rodriguez to stripe the parking lot in wide yellow lines, indicating in clear, large, yellow lettering, 'Park at Your Own Risk—Flood Zone.' These warnings were painted on the black top in six different locations." He held up a blown-up photo of one of the yellow-lined, flood-zone, warning areas painted on the parking lot blacktop. "This was in addition to the numerous pole signs indicating the same. This in and of itself exonerates my client."

Kent smiled at Jerry's statements. As manager of the Las Vegas branch of Heath Sign Company, he'd landed the Caesars Palace interior sign contract for Heath. He was onsite at Caesars Palace on the day the yellow lines were being laid.

"However," Jerry continued, "I would add that, as many of you know, Las Vegas is an arid environment. The last flood of any significance happened years ago. The storm of which we speak and the subsequent flooding it caused came on not only unexpectedly, but in such magnitude of force and size as Las Vegas has never seen. It struck without warning."

He turned to the attorney who had viciously blasted Caesars Palace by implying, without evidence, that the pit bosses "would have floating crap games before they would interrupt the gamblers, flood or no flood."

Jerry stopped pacing and stood directly in front of the plaintiffs' attorneys table. "Raging flood waters reached speeds of thirty-five miles per hour. Currents slammed vehicles into one another, creating extremely dangerous conditions, with hundreds of vehicles being swept away in rushing water. Imagine hundreds of frantic individuals making the unrealistic and most certainly life-threatening decision to enter those waters. It would have only added to the chaos." He paused to allow his words to settle, and then moved in for the knockout punch. "It was the decision of Caesar Palace executives that no loss of property was worth taking a chance on the loss of even one human life, the value of which is incalculable."

He looked at the spectators gathered in the courtroom, then back at the judge and the assembled group at plaintiffs' table. "Once the flood waters subsided, the executives acted swiftly to make a place available for the insurance adjusters of all fifteen companies represented here today. They cooperated in a professional manner to satisfy, to the best of their ability, the needs of their guests. And miraculously, no one, I repeat, no one working, gambling, or staying at Caesars Palace was killed or hurt, as a result of the good judgment of the officials I represent."

Mild scattered applause filled the courtroom. It was quickly squashed by the judge.

The trial lasted six weeks and, in the end, Caesars Palace, represented by Attorney Gerald Gillock, Esq., was exonerated of any financial liability in the case. Disgruntled attorneys representing the insurance companies had the unpleasant task of informing them that claims made by their clients had to be honored and checks written.

One litigator had faced an army of opponents and prevailed. In one of the first of his many cases to come on the Las Vegas casino legal battlefield, David had defeated Goliath.

16

Heroes Among Us

By 1980, the population of the Las Vegas urban area had expanded to nearly 160,000. Communities stretched out east to west from Sunrise Mountain to Red Rock Canyon and south to north from Green Valley to North Las Vegas and beyond. Public facilities supplying services like water, power, and gas grew rapidly to accommodate the burgeoning demand.

Of the many public servants working to supply the needs of the rapidly expanding city, no group was more deserving of praise than firefighters. The fire department protected homes and businesses and prevented loss of life in a city stretching both out and up. Hotels 30 stories high presented new challenges and antiquated building codes placed newly built high-rise casino properties in potential jeopardy. Despite warnings from engineering and risk-management companies urging owners to voluntarily upgrade their hotels beyond existing code, corporations continued to focus on business profit above all else.

In 1980, both Dan Celeste and Jerry Gillock would play active roles in the days that followed a tragedy spawned by corporate apathy and overconfidence.

Construction of the 26-story MGM Grand Hotel and Casino (currently Bally's) started in 1972. It opened in December 1973. Seven years later, on the morning of November 21, 1980, a fire broke out in a kitchen at the hotel.

The Clark County Fire Department received the call reporting the fire at 7:17 a.m. First responders from Fire Station 11 were on the north side of Flamingo Road, right across the street from the hotel. They arrived in Engine 11 at 7:19 a.m. They were followed by more than 500 firefighters from across Clark County who responded to fight the blaze.

Dan Celeste remembered it well. He was halfway through his shaving ritual when the phone rang.

His wife Carolyn answered. "It's Frank," she said. "He says it's important."

Dan walked to the phone. "Good morning, Frank. What's up?"

"You're not going to work today."

"What are you talking about? I'm getting ready now. I'm shaving." Dan had weathered the early-morning calls when they came in back in the days at the Hilton. Seven years later, he was still getting them. This time, from the MGM.

"Look out your window. There's a fire at the hotel."

Dan felt the shaving cream on his face smear against the phone. "It's probably just a kitchen fire. It'll be out by the time I get there."

"Look out your window, Dan," Frank insisted.

Dan stretched the phone cord across the room to the window and looked out. He saw a large plume of smoke rising in the distance in the direction of the MGM. The blood drained from his face. As soon as he hung up the phone, it rang again.

This time, the voice on the other end was his stockbroker. "You want to sell?"

"What? No," Dan replied. Concern quickly turned to panic. "What the hell is going on?"

"Don't you know the MGM's in flames, Dan? It could burn down completely."

Dan hung up the phone. He rushed back into the bathroom and wiped the shaving cream from his partially shaved face. "Carolyn, get the kids and drive me to work."

Dan, Carolyn, and their two young children packed into his Olds 98. The closer they got to the MGM, the more obvious it became that the problem was real. Dan's heart sank. His saw his life savings, all of it invested in MGM stock, disappearing in the cloud of black smoke billowing into the air.

When the car reached Koval Lane, police were on the scene turning traffic around, away from the back of the hotel.

"I'll walk the rest of the way," Dan said, his voice cracking as he exited the vehicle and bolted for the MGM arcade entrance. He approached firefighters on the scene.

They firefighters already had the entrance boarded up and were frantically attempting to keep the gathering crowd of onlookers at bay. "Get back!" they hollered.

Dan looked around at the disaster looming before him. News vans were on the scene, videotaping the mayhem as the firefighters fought the blaze. Dan cringed. His father was a retired fireman living in New York and news of the fire would certainly hit the national news. He crossed the street and entered the Barbary Coast. He picked up a house phone and sweet-talked the operator into placing a collect call to his dad. "I work at the MGM. I have to let my dad know I'm OK."

Once he'd spoken with his dad, he wove his way through the maze of fire trucks, police cars, and crowds of people toward a small motel on the back side of the MGM property. Originally a part of the Bonanza Hotel, the structure had been purchased and moved onsite during the original construction period, seven years earlier. It had functioned as headquarters for hotel executives as the hotel was being built.

Dan's heart was in his throat as he looked back at what little he could see of the MGM. Black smoke shot up through the 26 stories of the hotel, flowing out of broken windows and billowing into the sky. He gazed up to see furniture being used to smash through hotel windows, resulting in cascades of broken glass raining down onto firefighters and guests fleeing the fire-ravaged building.

He fought back panic over what he feared was to come. With 2,800 rooms, the hotel housed thousands of guests. As he watched people escaping the flames, he wondered how many were still trapped inside. How many wouldn't survive? He watched, heartsick with fear, as his future, the futures of his fellow workers, and the futures of guests who couldn't get out disappeared before his eyes in a massive cloud of smoke. At least he was alive.

Across the street, he saw Al Benedict, chairman of the board of the MGM, exit a vehicle and walk toward him.

"All the other executives will be coming here," Dan said to himself. At the sight of more MGM executives arriving on the scene, he felt a renewed sense of purpose. "So many people will need help. We've got work to do."

Hotel executives turned the structure behind the MGM into their base of operations. The phone company arrived to add lines, while local community organizations stepped up with food and clothing for those displaced by the fire. Volunteers answered calls coming in from all over the country from people desperate to learn if their family members were OK.

Tony DiOrio, MGM keno manager, called the school district to have school buses dispatched to transport victims to hospitals and temporary accommodations, where records of guests staying at the hotel were cross-checked with the relocated survivors. The scene was chaotic, but not without organization.

Dan worked daily with Al Benedict and other casino executives, using their years of decision-making experience to effectively address a myriad of issues, many serious, others random, as they arose.

But when Dan bumped into Jack Campbell, vice-president of finance for the hotel, he turned white as a ghost.

Jack saw the look of sudden horrific realization on Dan's face. "What's wrong, Dan?" Jack asked, alarmed by the expression on the face of a man he knew to be remarkably calm under pressure.

"What's wrong?" Dan replied. "I've been so worried about our guests, I forgot about my own situation. The hotel is gone. Hell, I'm going to be out of work here. I've got a wife, two kids, and a bunch of stock that's going to tank. How am I going to feed my family?" His head dropped.

Jack put a reassuring hand on Dan's shoulder. "Don't worry about being out of work. We have BI insurance."

Dan looked up. "What the hell is BI insurance?"

"Business Interruption," Jack said. "All the executives have it. You're covered. You have a job. You'll be paid, no problem. Relax."

Dan's heart nearly leapt out of his chest. He could physically feel the weight of the world lifting off his shoulders. But along with relief came concern. He doubted everyday casino workers had "business interruption" insurance.

Jack smiled. "And don't worry about the stock. It'll bounce back."

The rebuilding process took nine months. Working side by side, Dan's interaction with Al Benedict grew to the point where Al began entrusting Dan with project after project.

Once the hotel reopened, Al called Dan into his office. He pointed to a chair by his secretary's desk. "Dan, I want you right there every day. You have a standing appointment with me at one-fifteen p.m. Anything you have to report, you report."

After the tragedy was over, that was the way it went for the following years. Out of the chaos, a friendship developed that far surpassed their employer-employee relationship of the past.

Dan had started at the MGM in October 1973. Over the years, he told everyone who asked that, without exception, he felt good about the job and the company. His position offered him upward mobility working with people he respected. He continued his career at the MGM until its sale to the Bally Manufacturing Corporation in 1985.

****

Firefighters Save Thousands

Investigators determined that the MGM fire was caused by an electrical ground fault inside a wall socket in The Deli restaurant located on the casino level. Once ignited, it traveled up to the ceiling and the giant air-circulation system above the casino. Flammable furnishings in the casino, including wall coverings, PVC piping, glue, fixtures, and even the plastic mirrors on the walls, fed the fire. Within six minutes of the time of discovery, the total casino area was engulfed in fire, burning at a rate of approximately 15 to 19 feet per second.

The fire alarm never sounded. No fire sprinkler systems were installed in the high-rise tower, the casino, or the restaurant areas. Partial fire-sprinkler protection was provided for areas like the arcade, showrooms, and convention space on the ground level. Those sprinklers worked, but they weren't located anywhere near where the fire broke out.

Fire investigators concluded that, "With sprinklers, it would have been a one- or two-sprinkler fire," and would have been efficiently contained without significant damage to the property. More important, there would have been no loss of life.

Firefighters showed super-human courage, fighting under the most intense and deadly of conditions. They contained the fire within 45 minutes of its inception. Had they not, the entire hotel could have been engulfed in flames and thousands might have died.

After battling the blaze, 14 firefighters were admitted to local hospitals. An additional 300 firefighters didn't seek medical attention, but reported suffering the headaches, nausea, and dizziness characteristic of carbon monoxide poisoning. At least 10 firefighters also incurred psychological trauma from fighting the catastrophic fire; the actual number is considered by medical professionals to be much higher.

In November 2012, the *Las Vegas Sun* featured an article written by Dave Toplikar, commemorating the 32nd anniversary of the MGM Grand fire. In it, John Pappageorge, who was deputy chief with the Clark County Fire Department at the time of the fire, summed up his feelings about his fellow firefighters. "I absolutely believe what they did way back then was heroic. The fact that they went in and got so many people out was unbelievable. God knows how many more would have died if they hadn't have done that job. They are absolutely heroes."

Nov. 21, 1980, was a terrible day in the history of Las Vegas. The fire killed 85 people and injured 700 more. But it did initiate change. The fire revolutionized fire-safety protocol and codes in Las Vegas, in Nevada, and throughout hotels everywhere, with sprinklers and automated fire-alarm systems installed at a far greater number than in the 1970s.

****

Jerry Helps MGM Settle with Victims

Jerry Gillock's firm represented the MGM in the dozens of lawsuits filed against the hotel for hundreds of millions of dollars in damages.

The suits were settled in a $223 million fund that was given to victims and their families after the fire. Although 83 building-code violations were cited by investigators, no one was ever charged with any criminal wrongdoing.

Jerry's experience litigating the cases surrounding the MGM fire would prove to have a significant emotional impact on his life and career. The nature of the cases he took changed and his involvement in pro bono work increased. He began representing victims in malpractice and personal-injury cases, often fighting the likes of the casino companies and giant and corporations he had represented for years.

17

The Animals Steal the Show

At the dawn of the '80s, Las Vegas was accommodating tourists in the millions and the city was transforming once again. No longer just a gambling mecca for adults, a new family-friendly Las Vegas emerged, entertaining young and old alike in an atmosphere more akin to Disneyland than the land of Sodom and Gomorrah.

Circus Circus offered variety entertainment from noon until midnight, with trapeze artists flying over the heads of gamblers in the casinos. The mezzanine level included a large gaming arcade, complete with a popcorn machine, to accommodate under-aged family members while mom and dad gambled.

Entertainment directors city-wide insisted show producers modify adult-themed revue shows to answer the growing demand for family-friendly productions. This ushered in a new era in entertainment in Las Vegas: the era of "Sarmoti," which stood for "Siegfried and Roy, Masters of the Impossible."

Years before *Beyond Belief* and *Sarmoti*, Siegfried and Roy arrived in Las Vegas with a contract for a three-month gig at the Tropicana. They were booked as a novelty act in the Parisian-style revue *Les Folies Bergere*. They moved on to appear, once again as a novelty act, at the Stardust in *Lido de Paris,* then at the MGM, prior to debuting their own show, *Beyond Belief,* at the Frontier.

Curt Thompson was executive vice-president of the Summa Corporation at the New Frontier Hotel in 1981, when Kenneth Feld of Irvin & Kenneth Feld Productions and Ringling Brothers opened *Beyond Belief.* What happened behind the scenes during the many months of rehearsal leading up to the opening was kept a closely guarded secret, due in part to the number of wild animals featured in the show.

The two performers handled Bengal and white tigers, elephants, and other exotic creatures with skill and pizazz, but the unpredictability of the animals occasionally caused unexpected snags in the performances. Both during the show and in rehearsal, the results were sometimes comical, sometimes horrifying.

During the rehearsal periods in particular, the stagehands and showroom employees experienced out-of-the-ordinary moments on an almost daily basis. From tigers being walked on leashes to their cages backstage to lines of dancers rehearsing while dodging stagehands in the midst of set construction, there was never a dull moment in the Frontier showroom.

The same held true for hotel maintenance, inside and outside the property. Gene Sagas, assistant chief engineer at the Frontier, had been first introduced to Kent Carmichael by Curt Thompson. The reader unit section of the Frontier pylon sign was undergoing a huge modification to advertise the opening of *Beyond Belief.* Interior signs for the new show were being hung as well. As a result, Gene and Kent worked together extensively to facilitate the changes, while causing the least inconvenience to guests and employees.

As a facilities chief, Gene oversaw a crew of 30 maintenance personnel. His job was to keep all mechanical and electrical aspects of the hotel running smoothly, including boilers, electric motors, elevators, plumbing, landscaping, and any other issues related to the facility. This included the showroom.

Once the *Beyond Belief* contract was signed, work on modifications to the showroom began. The sheer size and scope of the production being created for Siegfried and Roy required a complete transformation of the stage. Stagehands worked overtime building the sets and props that would make the show come to life. They installed trap doors, elevators, and black-out curtains. Much of the labor came under the supervision of the set designer, working in tandem with hotel maintenance employees, all under Gene's supervision.

Gene spent months working with stagehands to build escape hatches in the floor leading to perches under the stage. The route was designed to allow Roy to disappear in a flash, only to instantly reappear, magically transformed into a huge white tiger. The illusions were created to thrill and astound the audience.

Building them was another story.

A month prior to the opening of *Beyond Belief,* Kent got a call from Bernie Yuman, Siegfried and Roy's manager. Bernie was a master at publicity and marketing, splashing advertising of the duo's upcoming show opening city-wide. He told Kent he wanted to do a promo shoot with Siegfried and Roy standing up on the pylon sign in front of their *Beyond Belief* lettering. "How high is that first platform?" he asked.

"It's about forty feet above the ground."

Kent heard a loud sigh coming from the phone. "That high, huh?" Bernie said. "Could I tell Siegfried it's, say, twenty-five?"

"Tell him whatever you like. But it's forty feet up to the platform."

"Doesn't matter. They'll do it."

The shoot was planned for the following day at 2 p.m. The four men would meet in the showroom, and then head out to the pylon.

The next day, Kent made his way to the Frontier showroom. He stopped at the foot of the stage.

It was a mess. Table saws sat on makeshift plywood tables supported by wooden saw horses. Dust flew as carpenters cut wood. Extension cords covered the floor in a tangled spider web of wire. Half-built giant props littered the stage, sandwiched amid cans of paint and neon-colored plastic paneling.

"Has anybody seen Siegfried and Roy?" Kent shouted over the noise.

One beleaguered carpenter looked up from his table saw. "Ask Gene. He's over there," he said, pointing to a hole in the floor. The carpenter grumbled something inaudible and returned to his project.

Kent hopped onto the stage and walked over to the closest hole in the floor. He looked down and saw Gene looking up.

Gene was cocooned in the small space with his head only a few inches below the stage floor.

"What the hell are you doing down there?" Kent dropped to one knee to get a closer look.

Gene ignored the question. "Help me out of here. I'm stuck."

Kent bent over and attempted to grab Gene by the shoulders. "Stop wiggling. I can't get a good grip."

Both men started laughing. It was a ridiculous scene. Kent pulled, while two stagehands standing on the basement floor a few feet below the hole where Gene was stuck pushed on his feet. He squirmed like a worm, inching out of the hole as the men pushed and pulled.

Once Gene was safely out of the hole, he looked down at the two stagehands peering up at him from the basement. "Sorry, guys. I guess I didn't fit after all."

He turned to Kent. "These poor guys have been working all week building this escape route under the stage for Roy. The carpenters finally finished the trap leading to his perch down there." He pointed to the hole. "Since Roy wasn't here to test it, I figured I'm about his size, so I volunteered."

"Going into show business, are we?" Kent asked.

"Very funny," Gene said. "Part of me was, for a minute last week, anyway. The crew building one of the show's illusions used my body to gauge the space needed to fit Roy." Gene sighed. "It must be fun, jumping in and out of props like he does."

He glanced back down the hole that had served as his own personal straight jacket only a few moments before. "I don't know how he does it, sliding down in those narrow crawl spaces."

"Neither does the audience," Kent replied. "That's the point."

Gene brushed the sawdust off his clothes. When he noticed the crew looking on, he crossed one arm in front of his waist, the other behind his back, and tipped forward in a comical bow.

Scattered applause broke out on the stage. Grumbles had turned to smiles.

"Maybe you should leave the illusions to the magicians," Kent said, looking down the hole at the long drop to the basement floor.

"Are you kidding?" Gene said with a broad smile. "And give up show-business?"

****

Sarmoti

Opening night of *Beyond Belief* was a huge event. It marked the first time magicians Siegfried and Roy were no longer a novelty act in a production show.

They *were* the show.

The phenomenal amount of money spent to build the sets, hire and costume the dancers, and incorporate the many exotic animals into one show created a landmark moment in Las Vegas entertainment history. Opening night was billed as a black-tie charity event, by invitation only.

Limos lined the Strip, arriving one after another at the New Frontier to deliver distinguished VIPs to the gala event. Gentlemen emerging from the limos in designer tuxes escorted women in sequined evening gowns into the casino. Precious jewels, draped on the necks of the women, sparkled under the bright lights of the hotel porte-cochere as the city's elite made their way into the casino. The parade of guests resembled a fashion walk on the red carpet at the Academy Awards.

The showroom buzzed with anticipation during the pre-show cocktail hour as every who's who on the guest list granted interviews with hordes of press before entering to socialize and be seen. Politicians and famous entertainers mingled with well-known sports figures and movie stars. Champagne flowed freely as guests chatted and nibbled on fancy appetizers from trays carried by formally dressed waiters and waitresses.

The atmosphere inside the showroom crackled with anticipation. Siegfried and Roy were perfectionists and, after months of grueling rehearsals under the direction of the two entertainers, the audience was about to witness a show-business phenomenon never before seen on the Las Vegas Strip.

Five minutes before showtime, an announcement came over the intercom: "Ladies and Gentlemen, please take your seats. *Beyond Belief* will begin momentarily."

Donned in his tuxedo, Curt Thompson watched from the back of the showroom as the front rows filled with figureheads. The prestigious group included the governor and his wife, two U.S. senators, the mayor and his wife, local philanthropists, wealthy socialites, and casino executives from neighboring Strip hotels. Joining them, front and center, sat all the top brass of the Summa Corporation.

The lights dimmed and *Beyond Belief* began. The curtain lifted to a collective murmur of delight from the audience as the scene revealed Siegfried and Roy seated on a lavish set, surrounded by 20 magnificent tigers. Then the room exploded in applause. The sight of so many beautiful tigers lounging majestically on tiered platforms covering a brilliantly lit stage in Las Vegas was breathtaking.

No amount of rehearsal can guarantee the actions of a wild animal, well-trained or not, and they were always conducted in the relative safety of an empty showroom. On this opening night, every seat in the place was filled.

As a result, inevitably, the unexpected happened. Thankfully, it didn't involve the tigers.

Near the beginning of the show, a segment featured Gildah, Siegfried and Roy's Asian elephant. Siegfried promenaded Gildah to the front of the stage, just as he had done many times in rehearsal. On cue from Siegfried, she rose up on her hind legs and trumpeted.

But for the first time, she sensed the huge crowd of strangers in what was normally a vacant space. Spooked by the unexpected presence of more than 1,000 people, she released a massive spray of urine, soaking the unfortunate VIPs seated in the front row.

Curt's mouth dropped. He stood in the back of the room, helpless to do anything, as he watched the crème de la crème of Las Vegas aristocracy being mercilessly sprayed.

Women who had spent the entire day and a small fortune being coifed, manicured, and made up by salons and hairstylists clutched their soaked curls. Their male companions made futile attempts to dry tuxedos stained in elephant pee with tiny cocktail napkins.

Showroom staff quickly supplied towels to the soaked VIP's while master showman Siegfried calmed the crowd. He even managed to make light of the mishap. "You are all very fortunate," he joked. "How many can say they've had this experience?"

Despite Gildah's antics, the opening night of *Beyond Belief* heralded the beginning of what would be a long and successful run. Rave revues and word of mouth resulted in packed houses for decades to come.

However, only three days into the run, the unexpected happened again.

****

Here, Kitty Kitty Kitty

The popularity of *Beyond Belief* stemmed from Siegfried and Roy's mastery showcasing wild and exotic animals. The show included one particularly rare breed of cat—the lepjag. The magnificent cat was a crossbreed of a leopard and a jaguar. He weighed more than 200 pounds and, as a crossbred animal, was highly unpredictable.

On the third night of the show's run, Roy stood onstage with the lepjag attached to a leash beside him. Without warning, the lepjag jerked his leash from Roy's hand and leapt off the stage. He shot up the showroom's center aisle in a streak of black fur, bolting past rows of frightened audience members toward the back of the showroom—his destination the kitchen. He reached the swinging doors at the entrance and pushed past them, entering the kitchen with ease.

Inside, unsuspecting kitchen workers had heard the screams of the audience and, at the sight of the beast, confusion turned to alarm.

The lepjag stood before them, his green eyes searching.

The strong smell of food emanating from the kitchen was everywhere.

The kitchen staff scattered in all directions. Servers standing nearest the animal jumped up onto the closest dishwashers and kitchen counters, knocking over pots and pans. Piles of dishes crashed onto the floor in front of the cat, spraying broken crockery in all directions.

The noise and chaos spooked the lepjag. He dodged the falling debris and bolted through the kitchen, past rows of ovens, sinks, and cooking stations. Rattled cooks and kitchen staff ran for cover behind the questionable safety of food carts.

One frightened fry cook, along with an equally freaked-out busboy, dashed into the freezer. They slammed the door shut just as the lepjag shot past.

They watched through the window of the freezer as the cat, following the scent of roast beef, jumped from countertop to countertop in search of his prey.

Suddenly, the kitchen door swung open.

Roy entered. He moved toward the cat and coaxed the lepjag from the counter top. He retrieved him by his leash and led him from the kitchen area. What had taken only a few minutes seemed like forever as the traumatized cooking staff watched the magician lead the cat away.

Roy handled the cat and Siegfried handled the audience. No one was hurt and no one left the showroom. For the two master magicians, it was all part of the show.

The performance resumed without further incident and the audience in attendance that night left with a unique experience, and a story to tell that could only have happened in Las Vegas.

Siegfried and Roy's many exotic animals graced the Frontier stage for years, but it was Gildah the elephant, with her legendary antics both off and onstage, who firmly established herself as the duo's most beloved animal attraction. She did it, as some would say, in spite of herself.

One evening midway through the first show, an inebriated customer who had lost his way in the casino staggered through an emergency-exit door and wandered outside to the back of the Frontier. With his drink sloshing in his hand, he managed to wobble over to the building's back wall. He leaned back and attempted to balance himself against it.

"Look at all the pretty colors," he said to himself, as he stared out through bloodshot eyes at the neon lights of the Strip.

The Frontier Back Forty, as it was called, was brightly illuminated by light poles. The glare of the lights blurred the man's already-compromised vision. He wobbled on unstable legs as he gazed around. He was raising his glass to drink what was left inside of it when suddenly, two large double doors only a few feet away from him swung open against the side walls with a heavy thud, one door coming to rest only inches away from him.

The man lurched back against the wall, squinting in an attempt to focus on the huge object coming through the open space.

"What the hell is that?" His eyes opened wide in horror as four tons of pachyderm swayed slowly from side to side, the enormous mass blocking out light as it headed straight for him. With each step the creature took, the ground shook.

The man stood paralyzed as the creature's huge trunk swung back and forth, brushing lightly against his face as the elephant passed by on its path back to the stables. Gildah continued her stroll back to the comfort of her stall and her waiting dinner of hay.

The man watched the elephant walk away, staring in disbelief at the animal's silhouette. It appeared pink against the bright lights.

"I'm seeing pink elephants now," he said, tossing his empty glass to the ground. "I've had too much to drink."

****

Gene's Evening Turns to Crap

As Franz Schultz led Gildah from the stage area to her compound, he passed by the drunk leaning against the wall without noticing the man. His attention was focused on his four-ton charge.

Franz was Gildah's handler. Part of his job was to watch every night from the wings as the elephant appeared center stage, all 8,000 pounds of her, drawing oohs and aahs from the audience. With a wave of Siegfried's hand, she disappeared in a flash of light, only to be instantly replaced by a smiling Roy and the thunderous applause of an astonished crowd.

Although the crowd's reaction to Gildah was a show-stopping moment for Siegfried and Roy, for Franz, the elephant was nothing more than a big job. Once Gildah finished her onstage disappearing act, Franz's responsibilities kicked back in. He was in charge of feeding and caring for her before, between, and after the shows. He was getting tired of piling up hay and shoveling elephant dung in the compound area in the Back Forty behind the showroom. The nightly routine was his least favorite task while tending to Gildah.

"There has to be a better way," he muttered to himself as he studied the perimeter of the elephant barn. "I have to get this area cleaned up."

He looked at his watch. It was a little before 9:30 on a Saturday night, between the first and second show. His eyes spanned the alleyway in front of him. It passed between the Frontier and Silver Slipper, and opened out onto Las Vegas Boulevard. Franz stared at the alleyway for several minutes. Sewer drains servicing both the Silver Slipper and the Frontier were placed strategically between the two hotels in the alleyway.

He walked over to a manhole just outside the double doors leading to the showroom and lifted the cover. "This will be a hell of a lot easier than shoveling up all this poop," he said to himself, smiling. "I'll just grab the fire hose and wash it and all this hay down the drain. Piece of cake."

Gildah watched from a distance, chained up by the barn and lazily chomping on hay, as Franz hooked up the firehose. He began hosing the hay and turds into the sewer. He stood, hose in hand, beaming with pride and satisfaction at his brilliant idea.

Five minutes later, however, Franz's brilliant idea turned to disaster.

The elephant dung, combined with the hay and water rushing into the hole, clogged the sewer line. A second manhole cover midway down the alley suddenly popped open. A river of sewage began flowing down the alleyway. It looked like the Busch Gardens log cabin ride shooting downstream. But this ride was shooting downstream right toward the Strip.

Franz looked on in horror as a as a river of sewage, from Gildah and more than 1,000 hotel rooms, flowed toward the main street of the Entertainment Capital of the World.

It didn't take long for the flood to reach the street.

When Les Granestein, a member of the hotel maintenance staff, opened the back showroom door to grab a quick smoke on his break, he looked outside and did a double take. He bolted out of the door and confronted Franz. "What the hell is going on out here? What's that smell?" He followed the spray coming from the hose and saw the mess shooting out of the manholes. "This is bad. Management needs to know about this. I'd better call Gene."

"Yeah, better do that, I guess. We got a mess here," Franz said. He kept hosing, as if he expected the problem to somehow wash away.

Les rushed off to call Gene Sagas.

"Holy shit," Gene said.

"Yeah," Les replied, laughing, "Holy elephant shit."

"Listen, Les. Get a hold of Abe's Sewer and Drain. Tell Abe to get down to the Back Forty right away and tell him to bring the pumper truck. I'm on my way."

Abe's Sewer and Drain pumper truck rolled to a stop behind the Frontier just as Gene was pulling into a parking spot beside the boiler room behind the Silver Slipper. Old man Abe got out of his truck, moving slowly. Heavy set and pushing 80, Abe didn't believe there was ever any point in hurrying. He strolled over to Les and Franz.

Les had joined Franz and both men were hosing down the alley.

Abe took it all in stride. He was a World War II veteran and a tough old bird. He was also a fiercely patriotic man. Plastered on the side of his truck were the words "Hire a Vet." All his trucks displayed the same slogan. Abe had dodged bullets and nothing else fazed him much.

He stopped in front of Gene and casually locked his thumbs behind his suspenders, taking in the unfolding drama. "Quite a mess you've got here, Gene. Turds everywhere." His tone was nonchalant, but there was a twinkle in his eye. "I see you've got reinforcements." Abe gestured to a maintenance worker at the Silver Slipper who had noticed the chaos taking place in the alley and grabbed a hose to keep the sewage away from his hotel. "Doesn't seem to be helping much, though."

Gene stood for a moment, shaking his head and wishing it would all go away. "So, what do you think, Abe?"

Old man Abe took another look around, nodding his head back and forth as he observed the river of shit still rolling down the alleyway and onto the Strip sidewalk. He slowly bent down, took the forefinger of his right hand, and wiped it along the ground.

Then he straightened up, looked Gene in the eye, and swept his forefinger in front of his nose. Taking a whiff, a huge grin appeared on his face. "You know what that smells like, Gene?"

"Yeah, I do. But I get the feeling it's not the same thing you're smelling."

"Yep. Smells like money to me. You're going to pay big time for this one."

18

Ricky and the Redstreaks

By the mid-'80s, Las Vegas had evolved into a full-blown corporate city. Businesses nationwide booked the Las Vegas Convention Center for their annual conventions, delivering thousands of businessmen and women from around the country to Las Vegas hotels for stays ranging from days to weeks. Las Vegas began winning bidding wars for events that drew significant revenue to the city by offering gambling and entertainment perks other cities couldn't deliver.

The massive computer show Comdex, the major Consumer Electronics Show, the automotive specialty products SEMA convention, and Barrett Jackson car auctions, to name a few, all opted for Las Vegas over other major cities nationwide competing for the business. Another major event that Las Vegas wrested from its longtime home in Oklahoma was the National Finals Rodeo, known popularly as the "Super Bowl of Rodeo."

The first National Finals Rodeos (NFR) took place in Dallas and Los Angeles between 1959 and 1963. In 1964, Oklahoma City successfully bid to be the host city. The world event remained there until the move to Las Vegas in 1985. The successful bid for NFR was celebrated as a huge win for the city. To this day, the National Finals Rodeo remains one of the most lucrative annual events held in Las Vegas.

Traditionally, December was the slowest time of the year in Las Vegas. But that all changed with the onset of NFR. Employees, normally laid off during the slow season between Thanksgiving and Christmas, now all worked to accommodate the thousands of rodeo fans and participants flocking to the city for 10 days in early December.

Casino executives anticipated entertainment to be a big part of the projected revenue and they scrambled to book the best country stars into their showrooms.

The NFR continued to grow annually, and, with it, so did the magnitude of the stars booked to perform.

During the years he held the position of executive vice president of the Frontier, Curt Thompson hired the acts to perform at the hotel when the NFR came to Las Vegas. The Righteous Brothers were already booked into the main showroom for the duration of the NFR when John Miner, Frontier president, spoke to Curt about entertainment for the lounge. As president, John represented Summa Corporation, a conservative corporate group. All entertainment booked at the Frontier had to adhere to its strict code of corporate standards.

"Curt, we need something special for the lounge. I want these rodeo fans in here every night. When you get back from your meetings in Colorado, find me a country band. I want a group that will reflect Frontier values and still pack the joint."

"Yes, sir," Curt replied. Curt was flying out to Denver the following day to meet with the Coors sports department in order to coordinate sponsorship events at the hotel during the NFR. "Once I have the Coors events locked in, I'll get right on it."

"Good. But, remember what I said. I want that lounge packed."

Curt headed off to Colorado. In addition to meetings, his trip included social events with the Coors marketing people. One night during one such event, he was seated beside the young woman who had just been crowned Miss Coors Rodeo, a bubbly brunette in her mid-20s. Her ponytail popped out from beneath her cowboy hat and her jeans clung to her curvy body, all the way down to her heavily rhinestoned cowboy boots.

"I can't wait to go to Las Vegas for the NFR," she gushed. "So many country stars will be there." She turned to Curt. "Who'll be appearing at your casino?"

"We've got the Righteous Brothers in the main showroom," he replied. "I haven't booked entertainment for the lounge yet."

"Oh, I know just who you should book," she said. "Ricky and the Redstreaks. They'd be perfect."

"Really?" Curt said. "Never heard of them."

"Are you kidding?" The young woman's eyebrows lifted. She gave him a playful poke.

Curt blushed.

Miss Coors Rodeo giggled. "You really don't know who they are?" She poked him again. "Mr. Thompson, Ricky and the Redstreaks are the biggest band on the rodeo circuit. They have a huge following. I guarantee you, if you put them in your lounge, they'll pack the place. If they don't break every attendance record in the book, I'll sleep with you."

Curt could feel the heat rising from the blush covering his face. Miss Coors Rodeo had made her point. He tried to joke his way out of what was turning into an awkward conversation. "I'm sure you don't plan on sleeping with a middle-aged man, a married one at that," he said. "This Ricky and his band must be something else."

Miss Coors Rodeo flipped her ponytail and gave him a flirtatious smile. "Trust me. If you book them, you'll be glad you did."

"Ricky and Redstreaks. I'll definitely check them out," Curt replied. "No strings attached," he added, still blushing.

Back in Las Vegas, Curt called for a promo packet on Ricky and the Redstreaks. Seeing their promo shots, he balked. The band looked more like The Village People than a country act. He watched the promo video. They were rowdy, raunchy, and loud, not exactly the kind of band he'd ever considered booking into the Frontier. But after only a few telephone calls, when he learned that Miss Coors Rodeo was right about their popularity, he decided to take a chance. He booked Ricky and the Redstreaks without John Miner's approval and hoped for the best.

The NFR drew thousands and, just as Miss Coors Rodeo had predicted, fans flocked to see Ricky and the Redstreaks in the small lounge at the Frontier. Her prediction was so accurate that Curt discovered he had a big problem.

The first night, disappointed fans by the hundreds were turned away when the lounge quickly filled to capacity. Cowboys, eager to drink beer and party, weren't happy. They left the casino in droves.

"You've got to do something, Curt," John Miner insisted. "We're losing a fortune turning these people away. Fix it."

Curt thought fast. He called Gene Sagas, his chief engineer. "Let's open up part of the Americana Convention Room and move the band in there. We can accommodate twice the crowd that's in this lounge," he said, as he watched the unruly crowd of cowboys crammed into the lounge, fighting for the attention of flustered cocktail waitresses.

The band moved the following night and conditions improved, but hundreds of unruly fans were still turned away when the convention space filled to beyond capacity. Gene warned Curt that if the fire marshals monitoring showroom events during NFR saw the excessive crowd pouring out of the area, Curt would have an even bigger problem.

"I want you to open up the whole Americana Room tomorrow night," Curt advised Gene. "The whole damned thing. How many more fans can these guys possibly bring in?" He looked over at cocktail waitresses loaded down with bottles and pitchers of beer, weaving through the unruly crowd. One of them shot him a look of desperation. Her struggle to squeeze through the throngs of cowboys gave him an idea. "And let's open up the freight doors. I'll bring in trailer trucks and park them outside in the loading dock. We can sell beer out there and give these poor girls some help."

On the third night, Curt stood next to John Miner. The two men looked out at a crowd of well over 3,000. The crowd was whooping and hollering as the band performed their biggest hit, "Moustache Rides." It was a racy tune and a racy show, hardly what the Howard Hughes Corporation would have chosen to entertain its guests. And when the band pulled out blow-up dolls in the middle of the show, John Miner spilled his drink all over himself. "Now, I've seen everything," he said, rolling his eyes.

The band was wild, but it was hard to argue with the numbers. Thousands of cowboys and cowgirls were dancing in the aisles and on the tables, singing along with all the tunes they knew by heart. When a band member led a sheep onstage, they cheered as if they were still at the rodeo.

"Well, it's not exactly what I had in mind, Curt," John said, shaking his head at the raucous scene. "I never expected to see sheep and blow-up dolls on our stage, but it's working. Good job."

Curt looked outside at the long lines of rodeo fans cued up at the beer trucks and saw Miss Coors Rodeo standing with a group of cowboys. He pointed her out to John. "We owe all this to that young lady. I'm going to buy Miss Coors Rodeo a beer to thank her." A slight blush appeared on his face. "No strings attached."

The band was subsequently booked every year for NFR by the Frontier. Ricky, a.k.a. John Jackman, and his Redstreaks continued to outdraw the country stars booked in the main showroom. From Tammy Wynette and Larry Gatlin in 1985 to Brooks and Dunn and Lee Greenwood in 2009, Ricky and the Redstreaks outdrew them all.

The funny thing about it was that they weren't even considered a country band. They were just great showmen.

19

Jazz & Jokes

The constant changes taking place in Las Vegas over the decades included the steady evolution of the sign business. Massive cookie-cutter reader units began replacing the unique and artistic signs of the past, reducing signage on the Strip to a row of oversized digital billboards. After years of working on iconic signs like those at the Dunes, Stardust, and Flamingo Hilton, only to see them imploded or torn down, the thrill of working in the sign business was gone. In 1989, Kent Carmichael retired from the industry he had helped build and moved on. But only a few years later, a friendship from childhood wooed him back into the Las Vegas casino business.

In 1992, casino gaming was still a primarily male-dominated business, so the renovation of one particular property was about to make quite a splash. A famous Hollywood actress bought an aging casino on Convention Center Drive, just off the Las Vegas Strip, and a lifelong dream was about to be realized.

The phone rang a little after 10 a.m. "Kent, it's Victor. You won't believe it but she's done it. She's bought the Paddlewheel."

Victor Smith and Kent had been friends for years. They met way back in the early '60s when Kent was with Ad-Art, servicing the sign at the Thunderbird, and Victor was the hotel's chief engineer. He was presently employed at the Paddlewheel Hotel, again as chief engineer, when he heard the news of the sale.

The "she" Victor was referring to was Debbie Reynolds. "As soon as this deal closes escrow, the renovation begins. It's going to be a bearcat. I could really use your help."

Kent and Debbie went back even further than he did with Victor. They'd grown up a few houses away from each other on Evergreen Street in Burbank, California. Kent had watched as Mary Frances Reynolds, the little girl down the street, became Miss Burbank, was discovered by MGM scouts, and transformed into Debbie Reynolds, America's Sweetheart. He held cherished memories of their childhood friendship, such as swimming in the Reynolds' Aba Daba pool.

Now, years later, Debbie was back in Las Vegas, not to headline in a casino showroom, as she'd done so many times. Rather, she was the proud owner of her own hotel-casino.

And so it began. With her son Todd by her side, the "Unsinkable Molly Brown" gathered her forces, called in her markers, and the transformation of the Paddlewheel into the Debbie Reynolds Hotel and Casino began.

Escrow cleared and while Victor and Kent worked to modernize the hotel rooms, fix the plumbing, and get the elevators up to code, Debbie began decorating.

Todd learned that a public auction was being held at the recently closed Dunes Hotel and had an idea. "Mom, grab your headshots and your autograph pen. We're going shopping."

Debbie and Todd, along with Victor and Kent, headed to the Dunes, where Debbie proceeded to buy practically the whole place.

She bought marble, banisters, furniture—and if it had a "D" on it, Debbie bought it. Soon, the floor of Debbie's hotel lobby was covered in marble from the Dunes. Glass doors with gold D's marked the entrances. Debbie selected unique items from her vast collection of Hollywood memorabilia to adorn the interior of the casino. She hung huge photos of Bogart, Cagney, Monroe, and other MGM movie stars on the walls of her casino. They'd been rescued by Todd, who had purchased them from the MGM Grand in Las Vegas after the devastating fire of 1980, where they'd originally decorated the halls of the upper floors of the hotel.

Debbie placed a plethora of other Hollywood souvenirs throughout the property, including two stunning chandeliers adorned with silver-dollar crystals from MGM studios, which she hung from the ceiling of the lobby. The chandeliers sparkled like a ballroom scene from a Hollywood movie, transforming the lobby into a glittering work of art.

Several months into the project, Victor asked Todd to meet him in the lobby, by the public bathrooms. As Todd approached, Victor stood beside Kent.

What's up?" Todd asked.

"We have a tiny situation here," Victor began. "Your mom has come to me with an idea, and it's a problem. I think you're the only one who can solve it."

"What's she come up with this time?" Todd said with a grin.

Victor shrugged. "Well, Debbie thinks these lobby bathrooms are larger than they need to be and it would be great to move the wall to make the lobby more spacious."

Todd knocked lightly on the wall with his fist. "Isn't this a retaining wall?" He gave Victor a quizzical look. "How much does she want to move it?"

"That's the thing, Todd. She only wants to move it six inches. And yes, you're right, it can't be moved without causing structural changes to the architecture." He sighed and leaned back against the wall.

Todd gave the slightly beleaguered Victor an encouraging look. "OK, leave it to me. I'll talk to her."

"Thanks. You know how your mom can be when she gets an idea in her head. I sure don't want to cross her."

Todd just laughed. "No worries. I've got your back."

Victor and Kent went back to work.

A few hours later, Todd stood with Debbie in front of the bathrooms.

"I just think it would be so nice to have a bit more room, Todd. It's not a big change."

Ever the diplomat when it came to his mom, Todd thought for a moment, knowing it was always a wise move to use humor as persuasion when dealing with the feisty entertainer. A huge smile appeared on his face as he looked at Debbie and landed his punchline. "Well, Mom, it's not one of your costumes we're talking about here. These walls don't have zippers."

Debbie laughed and the wall remained where it was.

In June 1993, two months after Debbie's 61st birthday, she opened her namesake hotel. The outside temperature topped 110 degrees so while Todd, Victor, and Kent scrambled to get final approval from the fire department to get the occupancy permit to open the property, Debbie stood in the heat outside the lobby entrance. She insisted on handing out glasses of water in paper cups to a huge crowd of fans, all eager to be among the first to enter.

As soon as the hotel and casino were running smoothly, the next step was the showroom. Todd spared no expense building Debbie's dream showroom, transforming the old Paddlewheel bingo parlor into the Star Theatre, complete with a one-of-a-kind fiber-optic curtain and state-of-the-art sound and lighting. But building it took time.

"We have to do something to entertain my fans, Rip," Debbie said to her dear friend, slapstick comedian Rip Taylor.

"I'm game," Rip said. "What do you have in mind?" Rip was more than her frequent opening act. He was a constant companion during the construction process on the hotel.

Debbie adored him, huge handlebar mustache and all. "Let's do an afternoon sit-down in the lobby, free to the customers who come in. We can set it up right under the chandelier, sing a few songs, tell some jokes and show-biz stories, sign autographs, and I can tell everyone about the beautiful showroom Todd is building for me."

The afternoon sit-down was a big success. Hordes of visitors scrambled into the lobby and adjoining casino to see Debbie and Rip pass hours entertaining their fans in an informal atmosphere.

When the showroom finally opened its door on New Year's Eve to usher in 1994, the place was packed. In addition to Debbie's family, among the invited guests were Steve Wynn, Robert Wagner, and Debbie's lifelong friend and fellow actor, Mickey Rooney.

Every night after the shows, Debbie signed autographs and took photos with fans outside the showroom, until the long line finally ended and she could retire to Bogies Bar in the casino to enjoy a glass of zinfandel, her favorite wine.

But Debbie wasn't finished. For years she'd been trying to find a museum to house her Hollywood-memorabilia collection. Although up until this point, her efforts to achieve her dream had not yet been realized, now she had her own place. Todd would build a museum inside the property to house the Debbie Reynolds Hollywood Memorabilia Museum. At last her treasures had found a home, and construction of the museum began.

Meanwhile, Debbie performed nightly in her new showroom to sold-out crowds.

Still, she wanted to do more.

In a moment of show-business inspiration, Debbie Reynolds found a way to recreate the lost magic of the late-night lounge. After her Friday and Saturday night shows, her 24-hour coffee shop, the Hollywood Palm Café, was transformed into a nightclub. Debbie called the late-night free-for-all "Jazz & Jokes."

Cocktail waitresses in fedoras and rhinestone ties served cocktails, while entertainers from casinos lining the Strip clamored to be a part of the mayhem. Debbie hosted the party every weekend, along with Rip Taylor and a trio of musicians. They shared a makeshift stage with singers, comedians, and Las Vegas personalities who poured in to party into the wee hours. Not since the bygone days of the infamous Las Vegas lounge, when Curt Thompson watched as the Rat Pack crashed Don Rickles' late-night gig in the Congo Room at the Sahara, had Las Vegas enjoyed the after-hours show-business camaraderie Debbie brought back to life.

The museum was completed and for a time, the legendary Debbie Reynolds, beloved by millions as both "Tammy" and the "Unsinkable Molly Brown," reigned supreme in Las Vegas. She achieved her dream and, in doing so, took her rightful place as a unique female entrepreneur in a city run by the most powerful men in the gaming industry.

She made her mark in Las Vegas history as more than a famous actress and entertainer. She owned a casino with her name on it, in Las Vegas, the Entertainment Capital of the World.

20

Everything Old Is New Again

By the early '90s, casino growth was starting to expand beyond the Strip and downtown. New casinos being planned and built in the outlying suburbs were specifically designed to target locals. These new properties attempted to ensure a repeat clientele of Las Vegas residents by providing better games, more comps, constant promotions, valuable giveaways, unlimited surface parking, and the kind of service that regulars expect, rather than the here-today gone-tomorrow attitude in the tourist corridor. Locals embraced the convenient neighborhood hangouts by visiting, sometimes on a daily basis, to gamble, eat, party, see shows, and put up their relatives in the hotel rooms. Movie theaters, bowling alleys, and retail shops and adjacent shopping centers, even daycare facilities were added, drawing local clientele into the casinos in droves

Although giant cranes continued to loom on the Strip's horizon, erecting even bigger hotels and residential high-rise complexes, construction also stretching to outlying areas farther south.

In 1993, Gene Sagas left the Frontier and was working at Binion's Horseshoe Club downtown. One morning, he got a call from Yvette Joachim, a young woman in human resources at the Mirage.

Yvette had established herself as a shrewd negotiator in numerous casino-related disputes, including some with the Culinary Union that arose at the Horseshoe, which is where she met Gene. She'd been hired personally by Steve Wynn to mediate a "union-versus-non-union" problem, when union members threatened to reveal all the magic secrets from Sicgfried and Roy's show, which moved to the Mirage when it opened in 1989, if their demands weren't met. She successfully led intense negotiations that ultimately resolved the Mirage dispute, satisfying the union and saving the Mirage millions in legal fees. This made her a valued employee and a legend of sorts in the Las Vegas business community.

"Gene, a Reno-based gaming company called Boomtown Inc. plans to build a new casino down on Blue Diamond Road," she began. "They need a local rep to oversee the project. I think it might be a good fit for you, if you're interested."

"Sure," Gene replied. "Tell me more."

"The group's VP of human resources is in town. His name is Don Dixon. I can set up an introduction, if you like."

Gene and Don held their first face-to-face interview at the truck stop located on Blue Diamond Road, across the street from the land where Boomtown Las Vegas was to be built. At that time, it was nothing more than an 80-acre vacant lot owned by billionaire Ed Roski Jr., president of Majestic Realty Co., the largest privately owned industrial development company in the United States. Roski and the Reno Boomtown team would build the property in a joint venture. After a series of meetings and a trip to northern Nevada to meet with Boomtown execs, Gene took the job. The construction of Boomtown, at the I-15 interchange with Blue Diamond Road one mile south of the Strip, began

Gene hired and supervised the workforce and oversaw compliance with complex Las Vegas building codes.

In the case of Boomtown, the complexities were many. They started outside. Strict rules governing parking, camper-land layout, pylon-sign location, and hotel delivery access were all monitored by the building department and other county agencies. Inside, the 300-room hotel, with registration desk, executive offices, convention space, restaurants, and a showroom, was subject to even more complex regulations. The casino was a beast in and of itself, with gaming regulations on labor, layout, and licensing all subject to a myriad of laws.

The Reno owners, still embracing the bygone era of Wild West casinos, lacked an understanding of the ebb and flow of gaming in the more sophisticated southern Nevada. The philosophy on marketing strategies and tourist needs in Reno, although effective for the state's northern city, differed from those in a much different Las Vegas venue. As a result of these differences, Gene had his hands full, fighting conflicting ideas on the manner in which to develop the property into a viable working hotel-casino. Reno execs nixed the idea of holding boxing events once Boomtown was completed, a move that could have garnered a fortune in profits like those being made by other casinos on the Strip holding boxing events.

While the hotel was in the early planning stages, in order to receive the OK by residents living in the community for the casino to be built, space for a grocery store was included in the plans. Roski, known to be a forceful and intelligent operator, championed the grocery-store idea, having learned that slot play in grocery stores garnered large profits, exceeding that of slot play in casinos.

However, once again, Las Vegas and Reno philosophies clashed. The Reno partners wanted a showroom in the space allotted for the grocery. When the original plans were modified to make way for a showroom,

Gene had a real logistical problem. He had to turn a long narrow space into a functioning entertainment venue.

He called an old friend. "Kent, have I got a job for you."

Kent Carmichael had just finished assisting Todd Fisher build the Star Theater for Debbie Reynolds at her newly opened hotel on Convention Center Drive. Todd had transformed the old Paddlewheel bingo parlor into Debbie's dream showroom and, during the process, Kent learned a lot about the complexities of showroom sound and lighting. Todd's finished product was heralded throughout the city as a theatrical masterpiece.

"Any chance I can lure you away from Debbie?" Gene asked. "I need someone who knows how to build a showroom."

Gene convinced Kent to join the team and use his lighting skills and construction experience to construct the Boomtown venue. The two men were once again working together.

When the Reno executives hired Curt Thompson as general manager of the new resort, Curt called his old roommate, Dan Celeste, and hired him as director of purchasing. This reunited Curt, Gene, Dan, and Kent, this time as one team, working under one roof, for the first time.

Dan brought his expertise in food and beverage management to oversee restaurant staffing and design, while Gene and Kent monitored the construction of hotel and casino facilities, all under Curt's watchful eye.

The group functioned well together and in May 1994, Boomtown opened its doors. The Reno partners, although pleased with the successful opening, continued to question the direction in which Curt wanted to take the Las Vegas property. They challenged everything from slot-machine placement in the casino to the hiring of seasoned dealers and pit bosses. With every objection, Curt found a way to appease them, frequently resorting to making temporary changes, only to return to the original plan when the new ideas failed to work.

At one point, a partner insisted on an interior-design concept for the guest elevators that involved a unique corrugated metal-and-paint combination. Curt knew that the material, in particular the bordello-like fabric, wouldn't pass state elevator requirements. Still, the elevators were decorated as desired by Reno, only to fail OSHA inspection. They had to be disassembled and redesigned to pass code in order for the hotel to open.

On May 27, 1994, after months of disagreements and compromises, the property opened.

As the first New Year's Eve celebration at the newly completed casino approached, Curt faced heavy pressure to deliver a lucrative holiday season. As the southernmost casino in the valley, Boomtown catered mainly to locals and the success of the holiday event was crucial to ensure the property's ongoing popularity. The Reno partners announced they'd be flying down and expected the New Year's evening gala to be outstanding.

Early in December, Curt called Gene into his office. "I want a New Year's party that will blow the socks off these guys from Reno. I'm counting on you and Kent to make it happen."

Curt was once again placing his trust in the two men. Thanks to some out-of-the-box thinking by both Gene and Kent, the showroom was the one area of the Boomtown build that had come in under budget. The Boomtown showroom construction had just begun when Barbra Streisand announced publicly that, due to her ongoing battle with stage fright, her upcoming live performance at the MGM was going to be her last. When Kent heard about it, he offered to buy all her show lighting.

"It's all going into storage for who knows how long," Kent said to Streisand's manager. "Let us buy it. We'll even strike it for you after her show."

Streisand's manager agreed, Curt approved the purchase, and Streisand's roadies walked away without having to rip 22 Intellabeams and 12 Track Spots off the ceiling of the MGM Grand Garden Arena. Boomtown got more than $25,000 in lighting for a quarter the price.

On the afternoon of December 15, 1994, Gene sat with Kent in the Boomtown showroom, discussing options for New Year's Eve. Since the opening of the hotel, the two men had worked side by side, booking acts for the showroom and lounge. "There's a band I want you to hear," Gene said. "I think they'd be perfect for the New Year's Eve party."

"Where are they playing?"

A familiar look of mischief covered Gene's face. "Let's take a trip out to the Gold Strike."

"The Gold Strike? Really?" Kent asked. His eyebrows raised hearing the name of a dumpy little outlier on the way to Hoover Dam. "How good could the talent be at such an old casino?"

"Trust me," Gene said. "You'll see."

As the two men drove the 30 miles out to the Gold Strike, Gene explained, "These guys are playing in the lounge."

Gene and Kent arrived and made their way through the casino. Well-worn carpet and vintage slot machines lined the casino floor. The sound of coins dropping into the ancient machines rang out. As they headed toward the lounge, Gene admired the machines and thought back to the history of the Gold Strike.

235

Built in 1958, the property had originally consisted of a service station, snack bar, gift shop, and cocktail lounge that housed six slot machines. A few years later, the site became an Old West theme park of sorts, housing a ghost town, wax museum, and railroad. An 80-room hotel was built in 1982, with another 80 rooms added in 1986. A new 16-story hotel tower had modernized the property, but the original Old West atmosphere remained.

The casino was buzzing with activity as Gene and Kent entered the lounge. Assembled on the stage before them, a combo of a half-dozen musicians sat behind bandstands, playing to a small crowd. Not one of the musicians looked younger than 60. The bandleader wasn't a day under 75.

"I hope I don't regret what I'm thinking," Gene said, looking at the men on the stage.

A female singer stood in front of the musicians. She appeared to be in her early sixties and had a silky voice, reminiscent of the swing era of the '40s. The players in the group, although weathered in appearance, were excellent musicians.

Gene looked around. He noticed toes tapping under tables in the lounge and people at slot machines nearby humming along with the melody coming from the stage.

"They've got a nice sound and the singer's terrific, but is that the whole band?" Kent asked.

Gene led the way to a table near the stage. "Let's find out." He waved a warm hello to the bandleader and gestured toward the table. They took seats in the lounge and waited for the set to end.

Once the set was over, Russ Jones, leader of the group, joined Gene and Kent at their table. Gene identified himself and introduced Russ to Kent.

"How can I help you?" Russ asked.

"Well, as I mentioned on the phone, we're from Boomtown. I've heard good things about you and your music and we're looking for an orchestra to book for New Year's Eve. Is this your whole group?" Gene asked.

The man's face lit up at the mention of a New Year's Eve gig. "For this gig here it is, but I've got lots of other musicians I can call. Most of them live in California, but I know they'd be thrilled to play a New Year's gig in Vegas. For gas money, a hot meal, and an eighty-five-dollar gig fee, each and every one of them would be happy to come."

Gene looked at Kent, then over at Russ. "Sounds fair. Can you get it together by New Year's Eve? That's only two weeks away."

"No problem. I just have to make some calls." Russ noticed Kent eyeballing the bandstands on the stage. "I have enough bandstands to cover the whole orchestra. They're in storage and might have to be touched up a bit, but yes, I can do it." His eyes gleamed with anticipation and Gene and Kent could tell that memories were flooding back.

Gene broke the man's reverie with a gentle nudge. "I'm taking a chance here, Russ, but if you think you can do it, I'm willing to offer you the gig." He looked at Kent, who tossed his head in the direction of the singer. She was sitting with customers a few tables away. "Of course, we'd want your singer to appear as well," Gene added. "What's her name?"

"It's Gracie. She toured with the big bands years back. She's got a whopping songbook." Russ looked through ancient eyes at Gene. "I promise I won't let you down. My guys are great musicians and I can put together a group like you haven't heard in years."

Gene saw something in the Russ's eyes. Old didn't have to mean no longer useful. He believed these musicians still had something to offer.

Gene took the plunge. "OK, Russ. I'll set it up with management at the hotel. You're booked for New Year's Eve. Twenty musicians and one singer. And you supply the whole band set-up."

After Russ left the table, Kent looked at Gene, gestured toward the bandstand, and winced.

Gene got the message. The set-up was clearly old and worn. "Once the band arrives at the hotel for rehearsal, we'll check out the bandstands. If they need to be touched up, we'll have hotel maintenance do it the day before the gig."

"You're a soft touch, Gene." Kent smiled at his friend. "That's what I like most about you."

Gene and Kent drove back to Boomtown to tell Curt they'd made the deal. Curt, who'd come from the Frontier where Siegfried and Roy and countless superstars had been booked for years, was in for a surprise.

****

But Can They Stay Awake?

Russ and his orchestra arrived promptly at noon the day before New Year's Eve. They entered the showroom and set up for rehearsal.

Strains of music resonated out into the casino as Gene and Curt approached the showroom entrance.

"Sounds pretty good, Gene," Curt said with a smile as the two men entered the showroom. But the smile faded as he looked at the stage and the bandstand in all its disarray.

The scene resembled a gathering of clothed skeletons from an episode of "Tales from the Crypt." Every head was silver or completely bald and most of the musicians looked as frail as the little old ladies playing bingo in the casino. All the other hotels were booking rock bands and top-20 pop stars for New Year's Eve. Going old school was a huge gamble.

"Are you sure this is going to work?" Curt asked. "I mean, I love big bands, but these old guys look like they walked out of a time machine."

Gene shrugged, "Yeah, they're all pretty old."

"Old?" Curt replied, his eyebrows lifting up from behind his glasses. "They're ancient. I bet every man on that stage is pushing eighty."

Gene defended the group. "They were all full-time working musicians in their day. Most of them played in popular big bands, touring the country for years. Quite a few of them played in orchestras on the Strip, backing headliners."

"Yeah, but which headliners?" Curt asked, shaking his head as he scanned the group onstage. "These men were in their prime fifty years ago. Who'd they play with? Benny Goodman? I'll be surprised if these guys can stay awake long enough to watch the ball drop tomorrow."

Gene turned to Curt. "Trust me. When Kent and I heard them play at the Gold Strike, they sounded great. The crowd loved them." Gene saw the doubt in Curt's eyes and stood his ground. "We've booked some great talent in here. You just have to have a little faith."

"You'd better be right," Curt countered. "If this 'orchestra' of yours doesn't pull it off tomorrow night, we could both be welcoming in the new year unemployed." He turned on a dime and stormed out of the showroom.

****

The Transformation

At 8 p.m. on New Year's Eve, Curt entered the showroom. He stopped dead in his tracks and stared at the scene before him. The place was packed wall-to-wall with customers. A dancefloor in front of the stage was filled with couples dancing to the music. Colorfully decorated tables were covered with party hats, champagne buckets, and bags of confetti. Hundreds of balloons in nets hanging from the ceiling waited to be released at the stroke of midnight.

The transformation onstage from the day before was nothing less than extraordinary. Twenty gentlemen in tuxedos sat behind freshly painted music stands. A logo and "Russ Jones Orchestra" sparkled on the front of each bandstand. Every musician sported a black bow tie. They held shining musical instruments and rocked them from side to side in unison as they played.

Strains of "In the Mood" resonated from the piano, harmonizing with trumpets, trombones, and saxophones. The steady beat of the drums paced the lively swing-sound filling the showroom. Silver-haired couples on the dance floor swayed back and forth, while other customers seated at the tables looked on in delight.

Russ stood onstage at the maestro's podium directly in front of the orchestra, waving his conductor's wand and looking very much like Guy Lombardo himself. Beside him was Gracie behind her microphone, elegantly dressed in a full-length gold-sequined gown. Her sultry voice blended in perfect harmony with the sentimental strains of the orchestra. The whole scene was reminiscent of vintage Las Vegas and, judging by the smiles on the faces of the crowd, everyone in attendance loved it.

"I'll be a son of a gun. Look at those men." Curt managed to smile through the glazed look of amazement covering his face. "Is that the same group we saw yesterday?" He turned to Gene, who was standing beside him.

"Yep. A gloss-black paint job on their wooden bandstands and some glitter to dress up their band logos did the trick." Gene's eyes scanned the rows of musicians, all spruced-up in their tuxes. "They cleaned up pretty well too, I'd say."

"I'll say they did," Curt whispered. "It's a blasted miracle."

Reno management was seated at a VIP table set up near the dancefloor. As expected, three executives and their wives had flown down for the celebration.

Curt and Gene approached the table and greeted them.

"Quite an orchestra you've got here, Curt," one of the executives said. "My wife loves big-band music and these guys are playing all her favorite tunes."

Curt felt a surge of relief. He'd spent months during the construction of the hotel and casino arguing with the men over issue after issue. He'd brought the whole project in on schedule and even managed to book a Grand Ole Opry show from Nashville to perform in the showroom. The show was packed every night and brought huge crowds into the casino. Still, the Reno executives always managed to find fault with something. Finally, on this night, they seemed genuinely happy. "I'm delighted your wife is pleased," he replied.

The executive's wife smiled at Curt. "What a brilliant idea to choose an orchestra that plays all the classics. And the mirror ball is such fun." She pointed overhead to an enormous mirror ball that was casting thousands of dots of sparkling light on the walls, tables and dancefloor. "I don't believe that was here the last time we visited."

"No, it wasn't," Curt replied. "Our showroom manager had it installed last night." Curt had hesitantly approved the purchase when Gene and Kent had insisted it would add to the ambience

Curt and Gene chatted briefly with the group, then left to join Kent and his wife at a nearby table. "Good job from both of you, picking this band," Curt said. "And you were right about that blasted mirror ball."

Gene sat down beside Kent. He pointed across the room at the dancefloor. All three of the Reno couples were dancing. "Seems the execs agree."

At the stroke of midnight, balloons dropped from the ceiling as the orchestra played "Auld Lang Syne." New Year's Eve kisses heralded in 1994 as couples toasted to the promise of what the future could bring. Gene wandered through the crowd and made his way to the foot of the stage. He looked up at Russ and saw tears of joy forming in the old man's eyes as he conducted his orchestra through the cascade of falling balloons and flying confetti.

"Everything old is new again," Gene said to himself, smiling. "Happy New Year to all."

21

Gene's O'Lucky Charm

By the 1990s, the Strip commanded 80% of the Las Vegas casino market, while most of the properties on "Glitter Gulch," the nickname given to the downtown casino district, suffered.

In order to entice tourists back, eight downtown hotels and casinos organized and formed the FSE LLC and started work on the Fremont Street Experience, and with it, the reinvention of Glitter Gulch.

First, Fremont Street from Main to Las Vegas Boulevard was closed to vehicular traffic. Then, a barrel-vault canopy was built over the new pedestrian promenade from Main Street to Fourth. The canopy was adorned with approximately 2.1 million incandescent lights and featured a sound system with 220 speakers.

Starting at dusk, visitors were treated to a brilliant light show, offered free of charge. New techniques were developed that made the curved images projected on the canopy visually stunning when viewed from the street below. The lights bathed the casinos of Glitter Gulch in a brilliant rainbow of color and quickly re-established downtown Las Vegas as a popular alternative to the Strip.

Fitzgeralds Hotel, a.k.a. "The Fitz," was one of the downtown properties involved in the rejuvenation. The casino opened as the Sundance in 1979. The owner of the Stardust and Fremont at the time, Allan Sachs, along with reputed mobster Moe Dalitz, founded the property, selling it to Reno-based Lincoln Management Group in 1987.

The Sundance became Fitzgeralds.

In 1996, Gene Sagas left Boomtown to assume the title of director of facilities and entertainment at Fitzgeralds. He took all the knowledge he'd gained while working at Boomtown with him. When casinos began organizing live-music events under the canopy, Gene, representing Fitzgeralds, came up with an idea that truly revolutionized the Fremont Street Experience.

It all started when the Las Vegas Convention and Visitors Authority, LVCVA, decided to do more citywide to promote tourism.

Rossi Ralenkotter, president and CEO of the LVCVA, scheduled a meeting at the Convention Center on Paradise Road. He invited entertainment executives from gaming properties city-wide to participate.

"Gene, it's Catherine." The voice on the other end of the phone was Catherine Gipple, Director of Marketing for Fremont Street Experience, LLC. "Ralenkotter's invited us to a meeting. I think we should hear him out," she said.

The two made plans to attend together.

****

Downtown Seizes the Moment

"Are you two lost?" Rossi Ralenkotter approached Catherine and Gene in the Convention Center lobby. "Follow me. The meeting's this way."

Mr. Ralenkotter opened the conference-room door, revealing a who's who of casino entertainment executives from the Strip. The group looked wide-eyed at Rossi, who was personally escorting two "nobodies" from downtown into the room.

Gene leaned in to Catherine and whispered, "Looks like we're the only two here from the wrong side of the tracks."

The initial meeting did not start out well.

Rossi Ralenkotter began by explaining what the LVCVA had in mind. "I've asked you here today to present an idea. We'll sponsor free-standing country entertainment venues at your properties, on the Convention Authority's nickel, in order to expand tourism." He waited for a reaction.

"That's what we're here for?" one MGM exec said. "We book our acts months, sometimes years, in advance. We just booked Jimmy Buffet in the Grand Garden Arena five years from now." He shook his head as if the whole meeting was a waste of time.

A Caesars Palace exec agreed. "Our showroom's already booked for two years out. We can't be bothered to participate in this. There's nothing in it for us."

Gene and Catherine looked at each other and read each other's minds. The LVCVA was willing to pay for entertainers to perform at organized events citywide at no cost to the casinos? It was an offer too good to refuse.

Gene raised his hand. "We'll do it. If the LVCVA is willing to invest in entertainment on Fremont Street, all of us at Fitzgeralds are onboard."

Catherine jumped in. "I can speak for the FSE. Fitzgeralds won't be alone."

Rossi nodded and addressed the rest of the group. "Anyone who's interested, let's talk." He flipped his hand in the air. "As for the rest of you, good day."

After a mass exodus of the Strip execs, Gene and Catherine remained to talk with Ralenkotter and set plans in motion. The LVCVA kept its word and booked country acts on Fremont Street, with Catherine and the Fitz leading the charge to promote them. Gene had his maintenance crew build a temporary wooden stage adjacent the Fitz casino entrance where bands could play and people could dance. It was put up in no time flat.

"She ain't that pretty, but she'll do," Gene said to his crew when they completed the stage. "What do you think, Mr. O'Lucky?" he added with a chuckle, looking up at the 65-foot-tall sign standing outside the Fitzgeralds entrance. The towering leprechaun, dressed in his green suit and red bow tie, sported a bald head and bushy eyebrows that peeked out from wire-rimmed spectacles. The comical Fitzgeralds mascot could be seen all the way down the corridor, waving his hat in the air and beckoning visitors to come inside the Fitz.

Country bands sponsored by the LVCVA began performing Friday through Sunday and weekends began to rock on Fremont Street. Visitors and locals alike gathered to party under the canopy. Adding to the funds provided by the LVCVA, the Fitz hired local acts and paid for advertising throughout the hotel and neighboring venues. General attendance at the hotel increased immediately. Mr. O'Lucky was showering golden shamrocks everywhere, in the form of keychains, casino chips, and beer mugs.

Then, a few months into the festivities, Gene had a brainstorm and Fitzgeralds hatched an ingenious plan. It would foster a turning point in the future of Fremont Street.

****

A Bar on Every Corner

Every New Year's Eve, Fitzgeralds hosted an event on the third-floor roof of the hotel. City VIPs, including City Councilmen Rory Reed and Gary Reese, along with Fitzgeralds vice-president Mike Darley and Gene himself, had a bird's-eye view of the fireworks and all the festivities happening along Fremont Street. The four men developed special bonds of friendship and Gene decided to call in a marker.

Gary Reese and Rory Reed were, at that time, chair and co-chair, respectively, of the Clark County Health District Board, so Gene set up an appointment with Gary Reese and took his newly hatched idea to the Clark County Health District.

He walked into Gary's office, crossed his fingers, and started his pitch. "The Fitz has been paying a hundred and fifty dollars for a special one-time permit to set up a temporary bar outside our casino to service the crowds during special events. I have to come down to get one every time we schedule something." He took a deep breath. "I have an idea that I know will be good for downtown and I need some help."

Gary told Gene to contact Paul Klouse, head inspector for the Health Department, to explain his dilemma and present his idea. On Gary's recommendation, Paul arranged for Gene to appear at a Clark County Health District Board of Directors meeting.

Gene once again pitched his idea, this time to the board. When he finished, the board, led by Rory Reed, granted Fitzgeralds a special permit.

He grabbed the first phone he could find and dialed Mike Darley. "You aren't going to believe it." Gene's voice bubbled with excitement as he explained what had happened at the meeting. "They did it. They gave us a permit for an outside bar on the street in front of the hotel. No caveats, no need for entertainment. We just have to build it."

"What?" Mike said. He nearly dropped the phone. "Are you sh**ing me?"

"I am not." Gene replied, chuckling to himself over Mike's spontaneous, albeit colorful, reaction. "This is huge. Naturally, the bar has to comply with code. But they passed a special regulation, just for us. We can have a full-service bar outside seven days a week if we want." He paused. "We have Rory Reed to thank for this one."

Gene and his crew got to work building the bar and what happened next is Fremont Street history.

The full-service portable bar was wheeled out and plugged in. It was loaded with all the amenities necessary to accommodate both the crowds that gathered for the shows Gene had booked on the hotel's mini-stage and the larger events sponsored by the LVCVA. When not in use, the bar was folded up and stowed in a safe storage area near the entrance to the casino.

The Fitz became the first casino to offer an outdoor bar on Fremont Street, legally servicing customers on the street. Mr. O'Lucky waved his welcome hat, as if playfully mocking the other hotels as tourists migrated down the corridor to the Fitz, where the booze was flowing like a river of green beer.

Other properties quickly followed Fitzgeralds' lead and soon outdoor bars appeared in front of every casino along the corridor. The Golden Gate stepped up the concept a notch, hiring sexy dancers in cowboy boots to perform on top of a specially constructed bar.

Word spread like wildfire about free entertainment and easily accessible alcohol on Fremont Street. As crowd sizes increased, the LVCVA booked more prominent country bands. Events that started out as weekend entertainment grew to seven days a week, packing the casinos and ballooning gaming profits. This prompted the Visitor Authority to keep throwing money at their country entertainment concept, combining events booked on the

Strip with the party going on downtown. Fremont Street quickly became known as "the street for country music."

One of the most successful pairings occurred during the National Finals Rodeo. As rodeo fans by the thousands flocked to Las Vegas for the NFR, the LVCVA drew them downtown by organizing "Hoedown Night" to kick off the rodeo. It took place on the Wednesday prior to the scheduled two weeks of roping and riding. A legion of country fans celebrated on Fremont Street throughout the entire two weeks, with casinos booking country acts in their lounges to draw the crowds inside.

If it was country, it was the hot ticket on Fremont Street and naturally, it was Gene's job to pack his showroom, so stacks of promo packages and videotapes often lay strewn across Gene's desk.

"Seems like every country entertainer in this city needs a gig," he said to himself, pawing through the piles of headshots and résumés. He stopped on a photo of a group of country singers, all decked out in cowboy hats and cowboy boots, holding guitars. *Country Superstar Tribute* was written on the bottom margin of the photo. He noticed immediately that each artist bore a striking resemblance to current country-music superstars.

Gene flipped the photo over and read the résumé stapled on the back. The group offered impersonations of Shania Twain, Tim McGraw, Faith Hill, Toby Keith, and a duo impersonating Brooks and Dunn. According to the résumé, the group had developed a big local fan base, "guaranteed to pack" any lounge in Las Vegas.

"Perfect," Gene said, picking up the phone. "If they sound as good as they look, they've got the gig." He set up an audition.

The popularity of country music on Fremont Street reached new heights in 2006. The Country Music

Association award ceremony had been held in Las Vegas from 2003 to 2005 at the Mandalay Bay Events Center, and moved in 2006 to the MGM Grand. Savvy LVCVA organizers took advantage of the appearance of country superstars on the Strip, booking them for concert appearances on Fremont Street.

"How did we manage to get that stage located right next to the hotel?" Fitzgeralds president Don Barden pointed at a prominent structure near the casino entrance.

The stage was one of two paid for by the LVCVA for the big events. The structure was a large trailer on wheels, with a fold-out stage and full lighting complement that was rolled in and set up prior to headliner events.

Gene pointed across the corridor to the Four Queens. "We've got one of the only two spaces big enough to accommodate a stage of that size." Looking up at Mr. O'Lucky, Gene added, "It's finally paid off, being down here at the end of the street. Must be the luck of the Irish, Don."

One evening prior to the start of one of the Fremont Street concerts, Gene was standing on the roof of the hotel, looking out over the massive crowd gathered for Sugarland's upcoming performance. The energy emanating from the street was palpable, with laughter and raucous commotion resonating off the walls of the barrel roof. Gene noticed people in the crowd looking up at the waving Mr. O'Lucky and playfully waving back at the oversized leprechaun.

What he saw gave him an idea.

He took the stairs down to the second floor and entered the Fitz showroom. The *Country Superstars Tribute's* first show was just ending. The crowd was dancing in the aisles, singing along with the performers as music blasted from speakers surrounding the stage.

"Thanks for coming," one entertainer shouted out as the number ended. "Don't forget to pick up our new CD, just outside the showroom. We'll all be out there shortly, to take photos with you cowpokes."

As the audience was filing out of the showroom, Gene waved the two Brooks and Dunn impersonators over to his table. They placed their guitars on their stands and hopped off the stage to join him. "What's up?"

Gene's face lit up. "Sugarland's about to go on outside. Grab your guitars and follow me."

Ten minutes later, Gene stood on the roof, once again looking out at the huge crowd gathered for Sugarland's concert. He looked down at the Fitz bar, backed up with long lines of cowboys and cowgirls buying drinks.

Suddenly, a woman standing near the front of the bar cried out, "Oh, my God, is that Brooks and Dunn?" She pointed up to the roof of the Fitz. Hundreds of heads turned to look up.

High up on the third-floor roof of the hotel overlooking Fremont Street, dressed in full costume and holding guitars, Gene's "Brooks and Dunn" were waving at the crowd assembled below. The crowd went wild, screaming and cheering, convinced they were seeing the actual country superstars.

Gene sprang in to action. The *Country Superstars* second show was timed to begin after Sugarland's concert was over. He rushed downstairs into the casino. "Get out there into that crowd and sell tickets to the second show," he said, handing two-for-one drink coupons to bellhops and change girls working the main floor.

A few hours later, Gene stood backstage in the Fitz showroom, peeking through the curtain as the audience piled in to see the second show. The showroom was filling to beyond capacity, with standing room only in the back.

Sugarland's concert had lasted two hours. The evening's second performance of the *Country Superstars Tribute* sold out during the first half-hour. Everybody wanted to see the two guys on the roof, the ones they'd mistaken for Brooks and Dunn.

****

Fang Furnishes the Fenders

As Fremont Street entertainment continued to grow in popularity, the annual New Year's Eve party under the canopy exploded into a huge event. Every year, the LVCVA booked the biggest stars for the event. After the demand for country singers fell off following NFR, rock took over.

In 2006, they brought in Smash Mouth, Chicago, Five for Fighting, and four other popular acts to perform for more than a million. And once again, Fitzgeralds was asked to play a role. The LVCVA needed a place to record live interviews.

Gene approached Mike Darley. "Rossi Ralenkotter wants to prerecord interviews with the singers in the Fitz showroom and broadcast them later on the canopy, just before the artists go onstage to perform."

Darley approved Gene's idea, but he went a step beyond. "Gene, I want you to go down to see Fang at Sam Ash Music Store."

The musical instrument store was located on Maryland Parkway and Karen Avenue. Phil Volk, a.k.a. "Fang," was the original bass player for the '60s rock band Paul Revere and the Raiders. He worked in the audio department.

"Let's buy some Fender guitars for all these musicians to autograph," Mike explained. "We'll have them sign two guitars, one for memorabilia to hang on the walls in our showroom and one for me."

Later, Gene had just returned from one of his many guitar-purchasing visits with Fang and was working in the showroom helping the sound techs set up for interviews when he heard a familiar voice. "Hey, Gene. Great to see you."

Toby Keith had entered the Fitz showroom.

Gene looked down from the stage. The heads of the hotel technicians all turned, first to Toby, then to Gene. Toby was a huge country star. And he was walking straight toward Gene.

Gene smiled. He was no stranger to country-music stars. During his years at Boomtown, country performers were the gold standard for both the main showroom and the lounge.

Kent and Gene had booked all the acts. Toby's first hit single, "Boomtown," landed him a gig in the Boomtown showroom when he was first starting out on a stage that had hosted country greats such as Waylon Jennings, Marty Stuart, and Porter Wagner, as well as the country-music revue produced by the Grand Ole Opry in Nashville.

"It's been awhile," Gene said, hopping down from the stage to shake Toby's hand. "After your interview, I've got a favor to ask."

"Sure, Gene," Toby replied. "What do you need?"

Gene pointed to several guitars resting on stands on the stage. He explained about the idea to autograph the Fenders. "Would you mind?"

"Not at all," Toby said.

After his interview, Toby signed two guitars, joining an army of other stars who did the same over the course of the years.

The collection of autographed Fender guitars that covered the Fitz showroom walls grew to more than 50, including rock stars Tommy Lee and Mick Jagger, country stars Sugarland and Toby Keith, and iconic bands Chicago and the Doobie Brothers, among many others. The collection was, in its day, comparable to the memorabilia presently hanging on the walls of Hard Rock Cafés worldwide.

****

Green Feet Mean Green Money

Of the many events booked on Fremont Street over the years, one holiday celebration in particular featured Fitzgeralds above all others. Every St. Patrick's Day, the Fitz reigned supreme over Fremont Street.

St. Patrick's Day festivities were in full swing as Gene stood behind the Fitzgeralds outside bar, pouring green beer by the pitcher-full for thousands of thirsty partiers.

As the beer flowed out of the tap and over both of Gene's hands, a bartender standing beside him laughed, "We're going to have green feet again this year. We've got a sea of green beer spilling out all the way down Fremont Street."

Gene looked down at his soaked shoes and kept pouring. "And green money's flowing right back into the casino."

Behind them, the hotel's giant Mr. O'Lucky leprechaun, hat still waving in the air, loomed over the throngs of people gathered to celebrate St. Patrick's Day.

Country music and a giant canopy played a big part in revitalizing Fremont Street. But those in the know believe Fitzgeralds, the little casino marked by a giant leprechaun dressed in green, along with the help of a real-life leprechaun by the name of Gene Sagas, brought "the luck of the Irish" to downtown.

22

Who Will Stand?

By the time Las Vegas rolled into 21st century, the population of the metropolitan area had skyrocketed to a million and a half people and the city was in the midst of a building boom that was unprecedented in the history of the world. Indeed, it seemed like the whole world was coming to Las Vegas to party and that the party would never end. But life in Las Vegas could also be a struggle for survival and dignity.

That wasn't the case for Jerry Gillock. After years of practicing law in a city famous for high-profile cases often garnering national attention, Jerry had become something of legend in his field. He'd litigated more than 800 cases and was a well-established and highly respected member of the Las Vegas community. He was selected by his peers for inclusion in *Best Attorneys in America* and received numerous awards, including the Nevada Trial Attorney Association's "Attorney of the Year" and the Lifetime Achievement Award for excellence in the field of law. He'd built a prestigious career within the walls of justice in the city he called home.

But one day in 2007, as a direct result of his many years of practice, an opportunity arose to make a real difference in the lives of a group of special Americans that stretched beyond the streets of Las Vegas. When he heard the call, Jerry rose to the occasion. It started during a meeting with a client in his law office.

Jerry leaned back in his office chair. His eyes were glued on the young woman sitting across from him. "What's the hardest thing you do in a day?" Jerry asked.

The young woman answered, without hesitation, but also without looking back at him. "Put my legs on."

Jerry shuddered. His heart ached as he studied the body language of the woman in front of him. She was so young and so damaged by the events that had led to the loss of her legs. As an attorney, this woman's terrible story was far from the only one he'd ever heard. Too many other stories were similar—stories of service members deployed, then returning home from Iraq and Afghanistan with devastating injuries.

At that moment, as he contemplated the obstacles the woman would continue to face throughout her life, he had an epiphany. On the wall behind him hung numerous certificates and awards received from local charities and businesses over his many years in Las Vegas. None, however, could match what she'd done for her country. "I have to do something," he thought. "I'm going to make a documentary. It's time for someone to help these amputees. Their stories need to be told. Maybe I should make a documentary."

He went home and discussed it with his wife. Then he started making calls.

Jerry began recruiting a group of Las Vegas entertainers to share in his vision and make his idea a reality. He started by contacting local Las Vegan Phil Valentine. Phil had previously written a movie for Jerry called *Paralyzed*, based on the horrific true story of two Las Vegas doctors who paralyzed 47 people during a competition to see who could do the most neurosurgeries. He called Phil and asked," Have you ever directed anything?"

When Phil replied that he had, Jerry made his pitch. "I want to do a film about the hardships facing amputee troops returning home from Iraq and Afghanistan. No money upfront, but I'll cover your monthly expenses. And I'll give you twenty percent of the net."

Phil, intrigued with the concept, accepted the offer on the spot. "I'll ask my buddy Michael Bedik to join the project as our photographer. He's a terrific editor as well and we make a good team."

Phil began writing a preliminary script, but early into development, the concept broadened. The issues facing returning combat troops were even more devastating than Phil first realized. He needed to talk to Jerry.

"Jerry, I'm finding that a significant number of new veterans, not just those with physical injuries, are suffering. Their issues are psychological. And they aren't getting the help they need."

After some discussion, both men agreed. The documentary would have to be broadened to include Post-Traumatic Stress Disorder, PTSD

"The only way we can do this story justice is to interview service members only, disabled American veterans, their families, and their doctors," Phil insisted. "No well-intentioned movie stars or sports figures with personal agendas. We'll have to travel. And it may get costly, requiring some serious bucks."

A look of resolve appeared on Jerry's face. If he was going to make this documentary, it had to be done right. "Do whatever is necessary to find the truth."

And so, in September 2007, it began. Phil and Michael would travel to cities across the nation, interviewing vets and their families, piecing together a film that would enlighten and anger, but at the same time inspire viewers into affirmative action on behalf of wounded veterans suffering from the devastating effects of PTSD.

"This documentary is going to be intensely personal," Phil said. "It has to show the good, the bad, and the ugly as we discover it. I've got a close buddy from childhood who's been a military doctor for years. His name's Walter Rustman. He'll be able to give us insight into what the service members he's treated have endured."

"Great," Jerry replied. "Start with him. Where does he live?"

"Midland, Texas," Phil said with a shrug.

"Fine. Go. What else?"

"We're going to need a strong theme song for this documentary," Phil added. "Michael and I can handle most of the soundtrack, but the theme song has to be powerful. It has to be a voice and a message that will resonate with folks and motivate them to support programs for PTSD vets."

The choice was simple. That voice belonged to Las Vegas singer-songwriter-entertainer Clint Holmes. The song was "Who Will Stand?" written by Clint after 9/11.

Jerry approached Clint and asked him about using "Who Will Stand" as the theme song for the documentary. As with Phil, Clint's response was an immediate "yes." Clint told Jerry that, as a veteran himself, he realized that most civilians rarely understood the scope of the consequences combat inflicted on service members and their families.

"Hopefully, the song will resonate with listeners," Clint said. "They have to be emotionally stirred into action. They have to feel something on a profound level. If I can help to shine the light on the needs of these service members and move anyone watching your film to help them, it will be my honor to do so. I'm in."

Clint suggested the title of the song would be a great title for the documentary and all agreed.

As *Who Will Stand?* progressed, Jerry wrote checks, while Phil and Michael traveled nationwide, interviewing, learning, and gathering hundreds of hours of footage. One trip was particularly eye opening for the two men. On Veterans Day, they visited Arlington West, located on the Santa Monica Beach next to its famous pier. It consisted of rows of white and red crosses beginning at the top of the beach and running all the way down to the high-tide line.

"Each white cross designates a fallen warrior from ongoing conflicts," an organizer of the annual event told Phil. "Because the number of dead keeps increasing daily and the space on the beach is limited, the City can't allow it to keep expanding." He pointed to a row of red crosses. "Each Red Cross represents ten fallen soldiers."

At the end of the day, Phil called Jerry and told him what they had experienced on the beach. "I had no idea the magnitude of what we are tackling," he said. "I wasn't prepared for what we've just filmed."

And the footage continued to grow, filling up with the personal stories of service members impacted by PTSD, either directly or indirectly. Out of more than 280 hours of footage and hundreds of interviews, 108 minutes made the cut.

The end result of Jerry's initial concept was a documentary that focused on more than a dozen service members who were either physically or psychologically wounded and the several charities, some of them local to Las Vegas, that assist them.

"I told the crew to follow their instincts and they did," Jerry said, during an interview. "They definitely created a film that is eye-opening, heart-wrenching, and inspirational. *Who Will Stand?* is a call to action that inspires the community to help those brave men and women of our military. Of that I'm very proud."

On the list of Jerry's contributions to society, as both attorney and social activist, the making of this documentary stands alone. Las Vegas is his long-time home, but his work continues to go beyond the neon lights of the casinos. Regardless of where his clients may live, he strives to achieve long-lasting results of moral value to improve the lives of those he represents.

Epilogue

Shortly after Kent's retirement from the sign business and years prior to building the showrooms at the Debbie Reynolds Hotel and Boomtown, he got a call from his old friend Gene Sagas.

Kent's early days of maintenance at the Fremont, crashing through the ceiling from the eye in the sky, and shaking in his boots in Ed Levinson's office were distant memories. Years of building the marquees lining the Strip had become his legacy. But a conversation over drinks with a friend and colleague returned him to casino life, and temporarily brought his career full circle.

Gene was still employed as the Frontier's chief hotel facilities engineer at the time and had just lost his chief electrician.

"It's a mess trying to keep up with all our hotel maintenance, so short-staffed," Gene said, as the two men sat sipping margaritas in the Frontier's Margarita Bar.

"I'll bet," Kent replied, giving Gene a sympathetic look. "You've got a big property here."

Gene set his margarita down on the table. "Look," he said, "I could sure use another good electrician on my staff. You want a job?"

Kent accepted the position of chief electrician at the Frontier, under his new boss and old buddy. The job was reminiscent of the old days back at the Fremont, keeping every inch of the property oiled and running smooth. It was like stepping back in time. And this time, the two friends were working side by side, from the casino floor, all the way up to none other than the eye in the sky.

****

Those Daring Young Men in the Eye in the Sky

Gene and Kent grabbed their tools and made their way through the casino and up to the mezzanine level of the Frontier. They stopped at the entrance to the secret stairway leading to the casino's eye in the sky. The two men opened the door and entered into darkness.

"It's black as ink up here," Kent said, temporarily blinded by the sudden absence of light. "We don't want to step on any bodies."

"Too late. I found one already," Gene replied, as his shoe brushed against a man lying prone on his stomach on the scaffolding of the catwalk. Gene stopped in his tracks. "Walter, is that you down there?" he asked.

The man on the scaffolding grunted a reply, "Yeah, it's me."

Walter was holding binoculars and peering down through the one-way-glass ceiling less than a foot below as he monitored play on the tables in the casino, looking for gamblers and dealers trying to cheat the house. The eye watched it all—blackjack, craps, roulette, baccarat, slots, poker. Even the employees in the accounting room were under constant surveillance.

Walter adjusted the pillow wadded up underneath his upper chest. "What brings you up here today?"

Gene wiggled his way around Walter, followed closely by Kent. "We got a call from one of the pit bosses. There's a ceiling light out over one of the crap tables."

Walter twisted his body up and around to the left to see Kent's long legs passing over him. "Hey, Kent. So, I guess it takes two of you to change a bulb?" he said, with a chuckle.

"You're a funny guy, Walter. We've got a camera out over the accounting room, too. Can't have that."

Walter struggled to find a comfortable position on the steel scaffolding.

"How's it going down there?" Kent asked, peering down over the back of Walter's head. "Anything exciting happening?"

"Nah, just a bunch of ordinary tourists today. No shady characters or card counters. Just some really bad blackjack players."

"I'll head over and check out that camera," Gene said to Kent. "Can you handle changing the bulb over the crap table?"

"Sure, if I can get Walter here to move over and give me some room." Kent waited for Walter's reaction.

"I'm nowhere near the crap tables and you know it," Walter said. His tone was playful. The men working the eye rarely had any diversion from their tedious jobs and bantering with maintenance was always a welcome change from routine.

"Just teasing, Walter," Kent said. He turned to Gene. "I'll get the bulb changed, and then join you at the camera."

Gene gave Kent a nod. His eyes had finally adjusted to the dark. He worked his way down the catwalk, leaving Kent to locate the blown bulb.

The bulb change-out went quickly. Kent lay on his stomach and reached down to unscrew the bulb from its fixture in a hole in the casino's glass ceiling, shielded from view from the casino below by the one-way mirror. Kent replaced the bulb and made his way down a second catwalk toward Gene's location over the accounting room.

"How's it going?"

"Take a look," Gene replied. He rolled to his side to give Kent room to join him on the scaffolding above the camera. "Definitely hot down there. Look at those poor bastards." He pointed down at one of the accounting tables where four men sat, shirtless, wearing long aprons with no pockets. In front of them sat stacks of money. Each man's job was to count a specific number of bills, wrap the bundles, and then place them in piles on the table. The aprons the men wore over their bare chests were undignified, but required. They made theft close to impossible.

Kent looked down on the activity. "Is the camera broken?"

"Yep," Gene replied. "We have to change it out. Too bad. I was hoping it was just a cloudy lens." He looked over at Kent and grinned. It was a long-standing joke among maintenance crews. Tampering with a camera in the accounting room was suicide for anyone working there. Stealing from any Las Vegas casino, whether attempted by an unscrupulous gambler or a dishonest employee, was a bad idea. Back in the mob days, behind closed doors, the punishment could be anything from a baseball bat to the knuckles to something much worse. But whether the establishment was run by the mob or a huge corporation, very few who attempted to steal money from any casino got away with it.

Kent and Gene removed the broken camera from its mountings. Kent rose to retrieve a new one from the maintenance room. "You keep an eye on all that money down there while I'm gone," he joked. "Back in a minute."

Kent made his way back down the catwalks, carefully avoiding other watchers lying prone in his path along the way, and exited the eye. He returned a few minutes later with a new camera. The two men worked together to mount the camera and hook up the wiring that enabled the live camera feed to the observers in the security office. Kent stopped to look at his watch as the two men packed up their tools. "We're nearly off shift." He helped Gene to his feet. "What do you say we hit the Margarita Bar before we head home? I'm ready for a drink after all this crawling around in the dark."

The two men backtracked across the catwalks and down the secret stairway to the security office.

Gene peeked into the room. "Everything working OK in here?"

"It's all up and running smooth, Gene," the security guard monitoring the cameras replied.

"Great. If there's nothing else, we're going to call it a day. See you tomorrow."

Kent and Gene clocked out. They entered the casino, passing hordes of gamblers trying their luck at the tables and slots. Both men looked up as they passed the crap table located directly under the replaced light bulb. Every seat at the table was taken.

"Look at all these gamblers, Kent. Not a one of them has any idea they're all being watched by the eye in the sky."

Kent smiled. "Ignorance is bliss, Gene. Let's go get that margarita. I'm buying."

ACKNOWLEDGEMENTS

The author would like to acknowledge the following individuals and organizations:

Unless otherwise noted, all photos contained in *Eyes in the Sky* are provided courtesy of Las Vegas News Bureau/LVCVA or UNLV Special Collections/unlv.edu.

To Kelli Luchs at the LVCVA, thank you for your assistance in gathering the iconic photos included in this book, and to Su Kim Chung at UNLV Special Collections, for hunting down that illusive cover photo shot of Norm from UNLV archives.

To the management team at the Neon Museum, thank you for taking the time to lend your support during the creation of this book.

To the Boys and Girls Clubs of Southern Nevada, thank you for allowing me to explore your archives.

Thanks to Todd Fisher, for graciously allowing the use of personal photographs from the Reynolds Estate.

To Jan Hogan, for your friendship, encouragement and proofreading during the early stages of this book. Thank you for sharing all your years of knowledge.

Finally, to Deke Castleman, my heartfelt thanks for your masterful editing, and for believing in this book. Your enthusiasm and unwavering encouragement has made the entire editing process a joy.

The Eye in the Sky

In 1968, while heading the publicity department, Norm Johnson organized a photo shoot in the infamous "Eye in the Sky" at the Mint Hotel. A two-way glass mirrored ceiling panel was removed from the flooring and a plywood plank laid across the catwalk girders in order to set up a shot of Norm surveilling gamblers in the casino below. The photo circulated worldwide and is believed to be the only one of its kind. (Photo credit: unlv.edu)

GERALD I. GILLOCK, ESQ.

Bachelor of Arts, Sociology
California State College
Long Beach, California (1966)
Juris Doctorate
University of Denver (1970)

ADMISSIONS
- U.S. Court of Appeals for the Ninth Circuit, 1983
- State Bar of Nevada, 1970
- Supreme Court of the State of Nevada, 1970
- United States District Court, 1971
-

LITIGATION
- Lead counsel in major medical malpractice litigation, product liability, fire litigation
- Prosecution of milt-defendant plaintiff cases
- Breast Implant Litigation
- Defense Counsel for Human Hospital, Doctors Defense Counsel for MGM Grand Fire
- Defense Counsel for Hilton Hotel Fire
- Company Insurance, INA, AIG, Universal Medical Insurance, UMC Medical Center
- Lead/Senior Counsel to Nevada Endoscopy Center/Hepatitis C Litigation
- Lead/Senior Council to HMO Litigation

Gerald I. Gillock, Esq. is recognized as one of Nevada's top attorneys.

He has been honored with Martindale-Hubbell's highest AV-Preeminent rating for his legal knowledge, analytical capabilities, judgment, advocacy skills and legal experience.

He has been named Nevada Trial Attorney Association's "Attorney of the Year" and has repeatedly been selected by his peers for inclusion in *The Best Attorneys in America.*

Mr. Gillock's personal contribution to the Las Vegas Community spans his entire career, beginning with his arrival in Las Vegas to found the city's first Boys Club of America.

He produced *Who Will Stand,* an award-winning documentary about Post Traumatic Stress Disorder or PTSD, sometimes referred to as a hidden wound of war.

Veterans returning home from combat often have the anxiety disorder which is triggered by a traumatic event involving death or injury. PTSD changes how the body responds to stress and varies for each person.

He financed the documentary to bring attention to the issue about the hardships returning troupes face returning home after experiencing extreme combat conditions and continues to be an advocate for improvement in the care these individuals and their families need.

EUGENE SAGAS

2018 to present – WESTGATE RESORTS,
Director of Engineering
2015 – 2018
HILTON GRAND VACATIONS CLUB, Las
Vegas, NV Director of Engineering

2013 to 2015 SPRINGHILL SUITES BY MARRIOTT, Las
Vegas, Nevada
Chief Engineer

- Responsible for all aspects of engineering operations to include maintenance and repair of equipment. Management of the preventative maintenance and general cleaning staff. Chairperson of the Safety Committee.

**1996–2012THE D LAS VEGAS Formerly FITZGERALDS
CASINO/HOTEL)**, Las Vegas, Nevada
Vice President of Facilities and Entertainment

- Responsible for all aspects of engineering operations to include maintenance and repair of equipment, purchasing and receiving activities. Responsible for booking all entertainment.

1993 - 1996 BOOMTOWN HOTEL & CASINO, Las Vegas, Nevada
Director of Facilities

- Managed department of 97 employees including Warehouse, Engineering, Porters, Bus Drivers, and Landscapers.

1990 - 1993BINION'S HORSESHOE, Las Vegas, Nevada
Maintenance Engineer

- Repaired and maintained Boilers, HVAC, Electric Motors, and Plumbing.

1980 - 1990FRONTIER HOTEL & CASINO, Las Vegas, Nevada
Chief Engineer

- Repaired and maintained Boilers, HVAC, Electric Motors, Plumbing, and managed up to 29 maintenance personnel

Throughout his professional career, most dear to Gene's heart has been a lifetime of advocacy on behalf of the children of Las Vegas.

He had the honor of being appointed the first Chairman for the Spring Valley Town Advisory Board, by Manny Cortez, former President of the Las Vegas Convention and Visitors Authority.

Gene also served on the board of the Vegas West Soccer Club, and has been an active participant in local sporting events for underprivileged youths.

An avid little league coach, almost immediately upon his arrival in Las Vegas, he began coaching little league baseball, eventually serving as Assistant District Administrator for little league, covering all of the southern Nevada region.

He was in charge of maintenance and repair of Shade Tree during the early years of the organization, overseeing the maintenance staff, in order to provide safe housing for women and children protected in Shade Tree locations.

Gene was formerly vice president of NAPE, the National Association of Power Engineers and, to this day, is the District Examiner for the American Society of Power Engineers, in charge of testing and oversight in Las Vegas.

He is the proud father of two sons, Alex and Michael, and proud step-father to his step-daughter, Meghan. Gene resides in Las Vegas with his wife, Maggie.

CURT THOMPSON

2016 to Present -The Longstreet Inn & Casino-General Manager

2002 – 2016 MGM RESORTS INTERNATIONAL, LAS VEGAS, NV
General Manager Railroad Pass Hotel and Casino & Gold Strike Hotel &Gambling Hall
Chief of Investigations Primm Resorts

1989 – 2002 HOSPITALITY QUALIY ASSURANCE INC., LAS VEGAS, NV
Managing Partner

1999 - 2001 FITZGERALDS HOTEL AND CASINO
Director of Table Games and Security

1996 – 1999 AMERICAN WAGERING, INC., dba LEROY'S HOTEL CORPORATION, LAS VEGAS, NV
Senior Vice President

1993 – 1995 BOOMTOWN HOTEL, CASINO AND RV RESORT, LAS VEGAS, NV
Vice President and General Manager

1992 – 1993 ELSINORE CORPORATION dba FOUR QUEENS HOTEL AND CASINO, LAS VEGAS, NV
Vice President of Casino Operations

1991 – 1992 BICYCLE CLUB CASINO, BELL GARDENS, CA
Vice President of Operations

1979 – 1988 FRONTIER HOTEL AND CASINO, LAS VEGAS, NV
Executive Vice President Hotel Operations

1977-1979 Aladdin Hotel & Casino Hotel
Manager

1967-1977 Del Webb properties to include The Sahara, The Mint and The Kuilima Hotels.
Graveyard Shift Manager, Sahara
Hotel Manager, The Mint
Hotel Manager, Kuilima Hotel

Curt Thompson is a veteran of 50 years in the Hotel/Casino industry.

When relocating to Las Vegas Curt enrolled in the first class of the hotel management school at UNLV. The school was then called Nevada Southern University with 15 students in the Hotel Management division.

He began his professional career in 1967 at Del E Webb's Sahara Hotel during the famous era of the Rat Pack.

While focused in hotel operations he shared his knowledge as an Associate Professor at Community College of Southern Nevada.
His career path led to various hotel and casino senior management positions in Las Vegas.

Most memorable and rewarding to him was as the General Manager that led a team of professionals in the design and operation of The Boomtown Las Vegas Resort which later became The Silverton Casino Hotel.

Thompson is still active in resort operations in Nevada and is a proud father of two sons and grandfather of two.

DANIEL J. CELESTE

Dan Celeste was born in Glens Falls, New York, a small mill town in northern New York State. He was raised in a family owned and operated restaurant business.

After graduating from High School in 1965, Dan went to a private junior college to study Restaurant and Resort Management and graduated with an A.A.S. degree in 1967 from Paul Smith's College.

In the fall of 1967 Dan moved to Las Vegas to attend Nevada Southern University (now UNLV) to continue his college education.

In 1969 Dan joined the first Management Team to open the International Hotel (now the Las Vegas Hilton) as Food and Beverage Controller. There he was instrumental in establishing food and beverage controls for the property. While at the International, Dan became associated with the late Col. Tom Parker and Elvis Presley serving as their liaison when they were in Las Vegas to perform or visit the International Hotel.

In 1973 Dan joined the Management Team at the MGM Grand Hotel as their Food and Beverage Controller and again established the food and beverage controls for the property. During these years Dan continued to pursue his Bachelor's Degree on a part time basis obtaining his degree from the University of Nevada – Las Vegas graduating in 1976 with a B.S. degree in Hotel Administration from William F. Harrah's College of Hotel Administration.

Since graduation from college, Dan's professional career has progressed in areas of Food and Beverage, Accounting, and Casino Operations. He has held positions as Food and Beverage Controller, Retail Mall Manager, Director of Purchasing, Assistant Food and Beverage Manager, Director of Food and Beverage, and Casino Shift Manager.

Dan has been active in community and professional organizations. He has served on the Board of Directors of United Way of Southern Nevada and has served as Chairman of its Allocations Committee. Dan has also served on the Board of Directors of the MGM Grand Hotel Federal Credit Union (now part of WestStar Credit Union) and served on the Supervisory Committee as well as serving as Vice President of its Board of Directors.

Dan is active in his church and was a member of the former Association of Italian Catholics. Dan has been active in the local chapter of the International Association of Hotel Accountants (now the Hospitality Financial and Technology Professionals). He has taught classes at UNLV's College of Hotel Administration in Food and Beverage Cost Controls and Food and Beverage Purchasing and taught Bartending Classes at CSN.

Dan is a former licensee and owner of a small successful gaming enterprise, former part owner and opening General Manager of the very successful Hooter's Franchise, and is an investor in real estate related businesses.

Now mostly retired, Dan keeps busy by helping his son run his pest control company serving as the company's accountant.

KENT CARMICHAEL

1997 to retirement, Olympic Construction, Contractor/QE for **Nevada Signs**, electrical **QE** for **Mammoth Air**, air-conditioning Company.
1994-1996 Boomtown Hotel, Casino, sound, lighting, electrical maintenance,
Showroom manager and Entertainment Director. Sound, lighting, electrical maintenance,
1992-94 Debbie Reynolds Hotel/Casino
Shift electrical engineer.
Imperial Palace Part time technical and electrical consultant
1991-92 Bermuda Island, Southampton and **Hamilton Princess Hotels.**
Theatre maintenance of electrical computer equipment for both facilities.
1989-90 Frontier Hotel, Chief electrician
Maintenance of steam controls, carrier air-conditioning equipment and surveillance cameras.
1988-89 Advance Sign Company, Las Vegas.
Marketing Director and Co-owner, CEO of service, maintenance.
1987-88 QRS. Corp., California, Maintenance supervisor
Electrical chief for Oceanside Branch.
1985-86 YESCO, Las Vegas Division
Electric messenger unit for **Caesars Palace**
1975-1985 Heath Sign Company, Las Vegas Division. Manager,
Director of electrical maintenance, service, installation and master neon.
1968-1975 Ad-Art Sign Company, Master electrician and **Manager** electrical maintenance, installation, sales, and service
1960-1967 Fremont Hotel/Horseshow Hotel
Electrician, swing shift in charge of "trane-centravac" air-conditioning power equipment and IBM Computer. **Western Neon**
Day shift, sign maintenance and sign hanger.
1958-59 Young Electric Sign Company Electrician

Kent was born in Los Angeles in 1933. He served in the Navy in the Korean War before moving to Las Vegas to pursue his career in the sign business.

An active member of his community, Kent coached Pop Warner football, high school basketball and little league baseball, as well as serving on the board of the Las Vegas Chamber of Commerce.

He is credited with supplying and installing the lighting for the old Gorman High School gymnasium and supplied two lifts to enable the installation of the lighting in the basketball court in the original Gym on Lindell Road, now the site of the Boys and Girls Club of Las Vegas.

Personal pastimes included boat racing, water-skiing, snow-skiing and classic car restoration. Of the many awards he has received over the years, his favorite is one he received at the 'Those Happy Days' classic car show, a charity event benefiting the UMC Children's Cancer Wing. He received a hand-made 'Best in Show' trophy, created by the cancer patients, for whom the event is held every year.

Kent is the proud father of two children; his son, Scott, a practicing DDS in Carlsbad, California, and his daughter, Shelly, a former model and lead hair stylist for Vidal Sassoon. He is the proud grandfather of three grand-children, Paul, James and Kirstin. Kent and his wife presently reside in Summerlin.

NORM JOHNSON

Norm Johnson was born in Burbank, California and grew up in Hollywood. At 17, he enlisted in the United States Air Force. He eventually became an investigator in the Air Police (now referred to as APIS), and arrived in Japan soon after the start of the Korean War. He worked on numerous cases involving narcotics, illegal trade of script (used by armed forces as money), and the printing of phony script.

On Dec. 17, 1953, he was discharged in San Francisco, and returned to live with his family in San Diego.

In 1955, Norm met **James Dean** while racing a Porsche for a sponsor in Palm Springs, and the two racers became good friends.

Norm met **Elvis** on the set of **Jailhouse Rock** in 1957, when he was selected to be one of the dancers in the Jailhouse scene. After filming, sometimes Elvis would discuss their mutual interest in the Martial Arts, and would also ask some of the group to join him in a touch football game, along with a few other actors, including Jane Mansfield, Mickey Hargatey, Nick Adams and Terry Moore at a Beverly Hills Park. After the film was finished, Norm and Elvis remained friends.

In 1959, Norm was hired to work in the public relations department for former **Heavyweight Champion of the World, Joe Louis.** He remained with Louis until 1963, for the biggest event ever promoted at **Dodger Stadium**—three titles were on the block: Davey Moore, featherweight champion, fought Sugar Ramos and lost his title.

Norm later went to work for **Copley News Service** as a reporter and sports writer. In 1964, he covered a fight at the **Olympic Auditorium,** in downtown Los Angeles, when a riot broke out over a decision. His story was selected as the **Best on the Spot News Story** of the year by **Copley Newspapers, Associated Press** and **United Press International** for Southern California.

On August 11, 1965, Norm was in the press box at **Dodger Stadium,** covering a baseball game with a friend from the Los Angeles Police Department as a guest. When his friend got a phone call about a disturbance in Watts, Norm agreed to drive him to the area. The resulting horrific experience prompted Norm to call in his first-person account of the mayhem. The headline, the next morning read, **"I Drove Through Hell Last Night**..." The article won many major journalism awards and was nominated for a **Pulitzer Prize.**

As assistant Sports Editor for the Las Vegas Sun, and featured columnist, Norm covered the UNLV basketball. In November 1965, Johnson was hired personally by Hank Greenspun to move to Las Vegas, where he did major stories on the Rebels' first major star, Elburt Miller.

In early 1967, he was hired by the Mint Hotel to be director of publicity for the hotel, at which time he created the world famous **Mint 400 Off-Road Race**

Over the years Norm has done publicity and management duties for entertainers including: Robert Goulet, Lola Falana, Wayne Newton, Freddie Bell, Mary Wilson of the Supremes, Charlie Daniels, Fred Travalena, Ray Romano, Gallagher, Esteban and Jack Jones, among others.

He continues to write his weekly entertainment column, "It's the Norm" which is in syndication and on the Internet. He is also the publicist for the **Laugh Factory** inside the **Tropicana Hotel,** working very closely with its co-owner, Harry Basil.

His proudest moments are having three great daughters, Robin, Denise and Lisa, five grandkids and at last count nine great-grandkids.

ABOUT THE AUTHOR

Karen Leslie is a long-time resident of Las Vegas. She began her education in journalism and creative writing in Dayton, Ohio.

She began her professional show business career in Montreal, and traveled extensively worldwide. She settled in Las Vegas in 1977 and continued performing.

Years as a professional dancer working on the Strip resulted in the formation of lifelong friendships within the industry, and, with them, and an appreciation for the history, growth and development of the city she calls home.

Within the pages of *Eyes in the Sky,* she hopes to share some of that magic with others, by documenting the remarkable stories she has been told by its contributors.

Manufactured by Amazon.ca
Bolton, ON

27947884R00160